'You have to open up and share your heart

'I'm sorry,' Jilly
that I find it so h

Zach hugged her
with your feeling
sweetheart. I'll never hurt you.'

He sounded so believable. There just seemed to be so much at stake.

Could she trust him? It was still only a maybe, but she'd have to try. . .

Caroline Anderson's nursing career was brought to an abrupt halt by a back injury, but her interest in medical things led her to work first as a medical secretary and then, after completing her teacher training, as a lecturer in Medical Office Practice to trainee medical secretaries. She lives in rural Suffolk with her husband, two daughters, mother and assorted animals.

Recent titles by the same author:

IF YOU NEED ME. . .
THE IDEAL CHOICE
THE REAL FANTASY
ONE STEP AT A TIME

NOT HUSBAND MATERIAL!

BY

CAROLINE ANDERSON

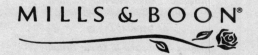

MILLS & BOON®

*First published in Great Britain 1997
Harlequin Mills & Boon Limited,
Eton House, 18-24 Paradise Road, Richmond, Surrey TW9 1SR*

© Caroline Anderson 1997

ISBN 0 263 80188 8

*Set in Times 10 on 11½ pt. by
Rowland Phototypesetting Limited
Bury St Edmunds, Suffolk*

03-9706-47433-D

*Printed and bound in Great Britain
by Mackays of Chatham PLC, Chatham*

CHAPTER ONE

JILL CRAIG was tired. Her head hurt, her feet hurt and she had been trying hard all day to concentrate.

Absolutely the last thing she needed was Zach Samuels.

She got him, anyway, strolling onto the ward with his lopsided, cheeky grin and lascivious wink, chatting up all the old dears and playing havoc with their blood pressure.

He didn't do Jill's a lot of good, either, but it was nothing to do with his boyish charm and everything to do with the size of his ego.

'If he comes near me I swear I'll kill him,' she muttered at the computer.

A chuckle from behind her brought her head round with a snap.

'Oh, Mary, you made me jump!'

Mary O'Brien, the cheerful, warm-hearted senior sister and Jill's immediate superior, grinned at her and perched her ample bottom on the edge of the desk.

'Zach giving you problems, Jilly?'

She sighed. 'Not directly. He just seems to irritate me every time I catch sight of him. He's so unrelentingly cheerful!'

'I know. Wonderful, isn't it? The old dears love him.'

'He'll kill them. Flirting with them like that—it's not good for them!'

Mary laughed. 'Rubbish. They adore it.'

'Yes, but they won't get better and go home! They'll all start inventing excuses to stay so they don't have to leave him!'

'And to think I imagined you were worried about their health, and you're just panicking about the bed state!' Mary chuckled again and patted Jill's shoulder comfortingly. 'Don't worry, sweetheart, you'll be off duty in a moment and you can escape.'

The thought was wonderful. Jill bent her head so that she didn't have to watch Zach flirting, and tried to force her attention to the computer. The recalcitrant beast was determined to mess her about, though, and she was ready to hurl a brick through it by the time his shadow fell across the screen.

His voice was low, distracting and extremely unwelcome. 'Hi, beautiful.'

Her teeth gritted. 'Not at the moment,' she said curtly.

'Oh, but you are, very beautiful—even when you're contemplating murder.'

She rolled her eyes. 'And you are juvenile and don't know when to give up,' she snapped.

He stepped back, hand on his heart. 'Ouch. You wound me.'

'I wish!' she muttered under her breath.

He gave a tiny grunt of amusement, and she threw him an irritated glance. 'I'm trying to concentrate. Do you have a problem that needs my attention?' she demanded.

He laughed then, soft and husky, the sound running along her veins like quicksilver. 'Oh, Jill, what a wonderful thought. . .'

She sucked in her breath and turned away, gritting her teeth. 'On the ward,' she growled. 'Do you have a problem *on the ward*? With the patients?'

'Oh, that. No. Mrs Jacobs is doing very well. I think she can probably go home tomorrow. Mrs Stevens is chugging along nicely now we've got her infection sorted out. She'd better have another couple of days on antibiotics just to be on the safe side. Otherwise nothing very significant is happening—on the ward.'

Jill refused to rise to the bait. She kept her eyes glued to the screen, tapping in garbage and fruitlessly backspacing to take out her errors. Two letters forwards, one back. Hell. Why didn't he just go away?

'Am I putting you off or do you always type this badly?' he asked from the region of her shoulder.

She dropped her hands onto the keyboard and a whole slather of junk leapt to the screen.

'Just leave me alone, Dr Samuels,' she gritted.

'Being formal now, are we, Sister Craig?' he murmured.

'It seems to be the only way to deal with you,' she muttered back, still ignoring him.

It didn't work. He walked round the desk and propped his elbows on the top of the computer monitor, staring straight into her aggravated eyes.

'Oh, my, you're gorgeous when you're angry. I wouldn't have thought grey eyes could flash sparks like that. Stunning with that fabulous blonde hair—fascinating. What are you doing this evening?'

'Nothing with you.'

'I hadn't asked you yet.'

'Good.'

He tsked gently in mild reproof, dangling his tie in front of the screen so that she had to stop working. Not that it was making any sense anyway. She sighed and folded her arms, waiting.

'You're being childish again,' she said after a long moment.

'A lesser man,' he said mournfully, 'would be damaged for life by your bitter tongue.'

'I don't get that lucky,' she grumbled.

He laughed again, and again the quicksilver shivered

along her veins. He reached out, his warm, hard finger catching her chin and tilting her head back so that she was looking at him.

She could have closed her eyes, but she met his instead. I'll stare him down, she thought, ignoring the fact that she was indulging his childishness.

'So beautiful. That blonde hair is something else. I'd love to let it down and sift it through my fingers.'

She tried to ignore the sudden leap of her heart at the image he brought to her over-fertile mind. 'Would you, indeed?' she said in what she hoped like hell was a bored tone.

'I would. Come out with me. I'll feed you—you're looking thin.'

'I've lost my appetite—nausea brought on by your sense of humour.'

'I'm hurt.' He looked anything but hurt. Laughter lurked in his eyes, the eyes with which her own were locked, and for the first time since he'd started work there two weeks ago she noticed the rich, startling blue of his irises, spangled with little flecks of gold-dust. A lock of almost-black hair was threatening to fall over his forehead, and his lean, angular jaw was shadowed with dark stubble.

He looked like a pirate, she thought inconsequentially, as if any minute now he would sweep her up and carry her into his cabin and do all sorts of outrageous and wonderful things to her—

She felt the heat in her cheeks and tried to look away, but his finger was still there, propping her chin, his grin widening knowingly.

'Maybe another night,' he said softly, and released her, wandering out of the ward with his hands stuffed in his pockets and a quick quip for the ladies near the door, while the skin of her chin tingled where his finger had been and her pulse tripped irritatingly fast.

Jill let her head sink down onto her arms and sighed.

'I thought you were immune?'

'I am,' she told Mary firmly, lifting her head to look at her colleague. 'I am totally immune, especially to hyperactive schoolboys masquerading as registrars.'

'So why the pretty blush?'

Jill glared at her. 'It's not a pretty blush, I'm hot!'

'Of course, dear, sure you are.'

Jill sighed again. 'He's just—so—'

'Gorgeous?'

She stared at Mary in amazement. 'Gorgeous? Zach Samuels?' She laughed. 'I can think of plenty of words to use to describe him, and gorgeous isn't one of them! Try irritating, self-opinionated, egotistical, juvenile—'

'My, my, he's really got under your skin,' Mary said softly, and to her enormous irritation Jill felt the blush crawl up her neck again.

'Hardly,' she said drily, and turned away, back to the hated computer that refused to co-operate.

'Go on, I'll do this. You're not making a lot of sense on it today. I'll let you go five minutes early in the interests of sanity. Otherwise you'll crash the whole system.'

Jill snorted. 'Tell me about it! Are you sure, though?'

Mary nodded. 'You go and have a nice hot bath and change into something glamorous for your concert with Gordon.'

Gordon. Jill had forgotten him completely. Oh, hell. She forced a smile and pushed the chair back. 'Thanks, Mary. I owe you one.'

She tidied up the desk, collected her things from her locker and made her way across the hospital grounds to the back entrance then over the road to the little cul-de-sac where her flat was. She was just stepping up onto the kerb when a car pulled up behind her.

'Can I give you a lift home?'

Him again. She turned slightly without breaking her stride. 'No, thanks. I live here.'

She waved at the house opposite, and then could have kicked herself for giving it away.

'In which case you could invite me in for coffee,' he said with a grin that she positively did *not* find charming at all! He was half lying across the passenger seat, talking to her out of the open window and paying scant attention to the road as the car crept along beside her. She stopped and glared at him.

'I could have you arrested for kerb-crawling,' she said crossly.

The grin just widened, those damnable blue eyes crinkling at the edges and that full, firm mouth twitching with laughter. 'You could keep me out of prison by inviting me in.'

'No, I couldn't. Anyway, I haven't got time to waste. I'm going out.'

'So you changed your mind! What time shall I pick you up?'

'Not with you, idiot.'

His face fell. 'I'm heartbroken. Who's the lucky man?'

'Gordon Furlow.'

'Furlow—public health? Dear God. You must be desperate. Don't tell me, he's taking you to the opera.'

She felt the blush and could have kicked the side of his car. 'Actually, it's a concert.'

'Wow. Tina Turner? Dire Straits? Rod Stewart?'

'The Suffolk Youth Orchestra, actually. His nephew's playing.'

'Ah. Family loyalty. Admirable.'

'I don't have to take this from you,' she muttered, and turned away, crossing the cul-de-sac quickly and letting herself in through her front door. As the door was closing she heard his voice call.

'Have fun. Try not to fall asleep!'

She slammed the door with some force and turned to lean on it. How did he manage it? Nobody else— nobody—had ever got under her skin like that and driven her insane the way Zach did with such consummate ease. He seemed to target her vulnerable spots with such devastating accuracy!

For instance, how did he know that just the thought of tonight's concert was enough to send her to sleep, far less the reality of it? Oh, hell, she thought, and trudged wearily through to the kitchen at the back of her flat, and opened the back door. The garden was flooded with sunshine, the first inkling of spring, and although it wasn't really warm enough to have the door open at that time of day it was, nevertheless, gorgeous to see the sun at last after the long and chilling winter.

She made a cup of tea and took it out into the garden, sitting on the crumbling little bench under the kitchen window and turning her face up to the sun.

She had to tug her cardigan tighter round her shoulders, and she turned her collar up and snuggled down out of the chilly breeze, but she wouldn't have gone in for the world. She looked around at the beds and saw weeds struggling to the surface. She'd have to get to grips with it soon, she thought, and shut her eyes. Not now, though. Now was for resting—

'Damn, who's that?'

She put her cup down on the bench and hurried to the front door just as the bell rang again. Zach, she thought, and snatched the door open angrily, then fell back a step in surprise.

'Gordon! You're early!'

The tall, lanky man ran a bony hand through his fair hair and sighed. 'Yes. Well, no, actually. I'm sorry, I'm going to have to call off this concert. I told Mother about it and she was quite annoyed I wasn't taking her. I hope you understand.'

She caught her jaw just before it hit the deck. Gordon breaking a date? Gordon letting her down? Wonders would never cease.

'Of course I understand. I hope you both enjoy it.' She held the door a little wider. 'Can I make you a cup of tea?'

He shook his head, and she was surprised to feel a little flicker of something that felt suspiciously like relief. 'I have to get home to Mother,' he was saying, and she wondered if he had always talked about his mother this way or if she was just noticing it because of Zach and his irreverent sense of humour.

Lord, she hoped not. She could do without a malevolent influence like that on her character!

'Don't worry,' she soothed Gordon now, 'you go on home. I could do with an early night, to be honest. Hard day.'

He looked relieved, and walked swiftly away down the path. She closed the door thoughtfully and went back to her cold cup of tea and the last few rays of sun. Had she imagined it, or had he also looked just the tiniest bit shifty and guilty?

And if so, why?

Zach left her alone the following morning. It wouldn't have mattered if he hadn't, frankly, because she was just too busy to stop anyway. On top of the run-of-the mill admissions and emergencies, they had one woman with multiple fractures who had fallen from a third-floor balcony in what the police described as 'suspicious circumstances'.

Her injuries, however, were not consistent with having fallen so much as having dropped onto her feet—or been dropped. Her heel bones were shattered, her lower legs were both sheered through and she had a slight loss of sensation due to a crush fracture of the second lumbar vertebra. All of these pointed to her having landed on her feet, but for now how was still a mystery.

She was being nursed in a single cubicle to allow her to rest, and was scheduled for Theatre later that afternoon to sort out her lower legs and possibly her back—if the neurosurgeons thought it necessary. She had had an MRI scan of the area and the results were being discussed that morning. In the meantime Jill was specialling her, and during the course of her observations she noticed curious striped bruises round the woman's arms and wrists.

Fingerprints? Jill wasn't a forensic scientist, but she wasn't thick, either, and it looked very much as though the woman had been held suspended over the balcony and then dropped. However, when the policewoman came to talk to her for a moment, the woman denied such a thing.

'I fell,' she insisted in a pain-blurred voice. 'I slid off the edge. It was my own fault. I shouldn't have sat on it. I fell—really.'

Jill showed the policewoman out and told her about the bruising.

'I saw it,' the policewoman said with a nod. 'What can we do, though? If she won't press charges, we can't charge him for it. There were no witnesses.'

'Him?' Jill asked.

'Her husband. He's knocked her about before—always

doing it, according to the neighbours. If she doesn't want to testify against him, though, we can't make her.'

Jill went back to her post, filling in forms and checking the monitoring equipment. Mrs Birkett was well sedated, but clearly not sedated enough to make her abandon her story. She dozed while Jill watched over her and wondered what could have happened that morning and why she was being so loyal.

Fear? It had happened before. She felt sure that the woman was hiding something. It showed in her eyes when she was staring into the policewoman's face, as if begging her to believe the lie. However, Jill's first concern at the moment was the patient's immediate health care because she was very seriously injured and needed constant attention. Speculation would have to come later when there was time.

Shortly before lunch Robert Ryder came round with his team and examined Mrs Birkett. Zach, of course, was there, very much in evidence but for once not flirting with the patient. In fact, he seemed remarkably subdued, and Jill was relieved that he wasn't trying to make eye contact with her and generally make a nuisance of himself so that she was able to concentrate and give the consultant the information he needed.

He checked with Jill that Mrs Birkett was stable and had been conscious all morning with nothing to give rise to any concern, and then pulled up a chair to the head of the bed.

'Now, Mrs Birkett, we've had a look at the scan results, and we've decided to let your back heal on its own. You've been very lucky that there isn't any serious damage to the spinal cord, and the neurologist is very happy to let us treat it conservatively. Basically, that means you'll lie here and rest for a few weeks while it heals. Now, as for your legs, I'm afraid that's a bit more tricky.'

Mrs Birkett gave a rather weak smile. 'I had a feeling it might be. My back just aches—my legs are giving me hell, and my foot—' She shrugged expressively. 'Will I ever walk again?'

The consultant nodded thoughtfully. 'Oh, yes. It'll be slow, but you'll get there. Lots of physio once we've sorted out the mess in Theatre. You were very fortunate, in fact, that your legs took the brunt of the impact because, if for some reason, they hadn't broken your spine would have been much more seriously damaged.'

'Would I have been paralysed?' she asked quietly, and Jill could see the fear flickering in the back of her eyes.

Robert Ryder shrugged expressively. 'Maybe. Who can say? You're not, of course, and you won't be. You have done rather a lot of damage to your legs, though, especially to your right heel, and we'll need to build it up and put in a bone graft to help you to walk normally on it again when it heals. You also need both of your legs pinning to support the fractures while they heal, and then you'll have casts on them to hold them in place while it all settles down. I'm afraid you'll be stuck with us for quite some time. Now, is there anything you want to ask about?'

Mrs Birkett shook her head. 'No, thank you, Doctor. I'll leave it up to you to fix me. You just tell me what I have to do, and I'll do it.'

She looked defeated, as if it didn't matter what happened any more. Jill felt a great wave of sadness for the poor woman. It must be hell to be the victim of a violent partner, she thought. Infinitely worse than the victim of a faithless one—

'So, Sister Craig, if we could leave it with you to prepare

Mrs Birkett for Theatre at three, we'll get those legs sorted out this afternoon. OK?'

Jill and Mrs Birkett both nodded, and Robert Ryder disappeared, taking Zach, still quiet, with him. He smiled at her as he passed, but the wicked twinkle and lascivious grin were definitely missing. Jill wondered for a moment what had happened to change him so drastically but, whatever it was, she had no cause to complain. The new Zach was infinitely preferable!

She needn't have worried. The following morning Mrs Birkett was back from ITU where she had spent the night following surgery, and the old Zach was back in force.

She heard his voice on the ward and popped her head round the door, meaning to ask him to look at Mrs Birkett. She caught his eye and he nodded, then continued flirting with Mrs Jacobs as he walked towards Jill.

He arrived at her feet in a gust of light-hearted laughter, and she shook her head in despair. 'I preferred you yesterday,' she grumbled good-naturedly at him, and could have kicked herself for opening the conversation on a personal note.

His eyes searched hers, peeling her innermost thoughts away layer by layer—or so it felt—until she could have squirmed. Then he grinned. 'Sorry. I only do serious days once every ten years.'

She laughed, despite her better judgement. 'You're incorrigible,' she said.

'Yep, that's me. How's our patient?'

Jill cast a glance over her shoulder at the patient lying with her legs suspended in 'gutters', padding-lined troughs that supported the lower legs comfortably slightly above the level of her heart to prevent post-operative swelling.

'Sore. She'll be all right, I think, physically. Mentally,

I think she's taken a bit of a battering. Her husband's due in to visit her today, I believe, and I don't think she's looking forward to it.'

Zach frowned. 'What makes you say that?'

'She asked me if she was well enough to see him, and I said I thought she probably would be but that we'd have to ask you. She looked almost disappointed. I think she's afraid of him, and I think she has good cause.'

Zach took Jill by the arm and led her into the office, and she tried to ignore the warmth of his hand and the strange sensations skidding over her skin. 'You think he chucked her off the balcony?'

'No. I think he *dropped* her off the balcony. I think he held her by the wrists and dangled her over the edge, and I think she either wriggled and slipped out of his grasp or he dropped her. Either way, it was his fault.'

'What if she was hanging on to the edge of the balcony and he grabbed her by the wrists and tried to stop her from dropping? Have you thought of that?'

Jill smiled sadly. 'So how did she get the fingermarks over her left thigh? Or the mark like an open handslap across her side? No, Zach, he's been knocking her about and she's too terrified of him to spill the beans.'

'Bastard.'

The word was softly spoken, all the more shocking for the air of contained violence she could see in his eyes.

'You feel strongly about it.'

He laughed shortly. 'Just a bit. My sister was married to a real charmer. The last time he knocked her about she was six months pregnant. The baby's still in SCBU four months later.'

Jill's jaw sagged. 'Is your sister all right?'

His smile was wry. 'She will be, given plenty of support. For now she's just taking one day at a time. The baby's more of a worry. He's got chest problems. Anyway, about Mrs Birkett. How does she seem this morning?'

'All right. Her foot's a better colour since you sorted out the circulation yesterday, and she says it's a bit more comfortable but I'm sure that's just because Robert's upped the pain relief now.'

'Whatever works. I fail to see why she should suffer just because some swine decided to murder her.' He gave Jill a slightly strained smile. 'Let's go and see her, shall we? I'm sure we'll find she isn't well enough to see her husband, at least for more than a few moments under supervision.'

His examination was thorough but gentle, his bedside manner for once not grating on Jill's nerves, and she wondered if it was because he'd given her a brief insight into his real feelings about something, rather than the superficial cheer that permeated his usual manner.

He left the ward immediately after looking at Mrs Birkett, called away to A and E for an emergency, and Jill was left to settle down again with her patient and concentrate on her post-operative care.

Because of the extent of her surgery to realign the bones in her legs and right heel, it was very important to monitor the condition of her feet regularly and make sure there was no swelling or discoloration of the healthy tissues. It was a difficult job because the whole of both feet were swollen and discoloured anyway, following the impact with the ground, and it was a case of looking for further change rather than anything abnormal. Indeed, there was very little below the level of her knees which could have been described as normal, and the pain must have been awful.

She would have a pethidine pump to control her own pain relief once she was a little further towards recovery, but until then Jill was monitoring the dosage of a more powerful morphine-type drug and maintaining it at an appropriate level. There were wound drains to check and an intravenous drip to keep an eye on, as well as the monitors for her vital functions such as heart rhythm, temperature, blood pressure and respiration rate. Modern technology took much of the contact out of nursing, Jill thought, but all the machines needed watching for any abnormality that might indicate a problem.

It was absorbing and required concentration, but even so Jill found her thoughts straying every now and again to the new Zach she had glimpsed. Which was the real man? Was it possible that he wasn't the superficial, pleasure-seeking flirt she had him pegged as?

Then she heard his voice on the ward again, teasing and cajoling one of the nurses, his laughter impertinent and— damn it—infectious. She wiped the smile off her face. No. That was the real Zach out there now, brash and confident, full of his own wit.

She would *not* smile!

It was a long day again. Every day seemed to be long now, for some reason. Perhaps she needed a holiday.

Mr Birkett had come in, a big, strong man with hands like hams, and had been most indignant that Jill had refused to leave the room. 'I have to be here at all times,' she'd explained patiently. 'Your wife has very serious injuries, Mr Birkett. She needs constant monitoring. We wouldn't want anything else to happen to her, would we?'

Had she imagined it, or had a look of fear flickered in his eyes? He had bent over his wife, muttering urgently in her ear and seeming to plead with her. She had closed her eyes and patted his hand, then told Jill that she was very tired.

'I'm sorry, Mr Birkett, you'll have to leave now. Your wife needs to rest,' she'd told the man, and he'd left reluctantly, promising to be back in the morning.

It had sounded almost like a threat.

Her patient slept after that for a while, and eventually it was five o'clock and Jill handed over Mrs Birkett's care to another nurse and left the hospital.

It was another lovely day, or had been. She had missed it all except the last brief hours of early evening, and she opened her door again and took some tea outside into the garden.

Yet again, she was disturbed by the doorbell. Gordon again? She hadn't seen him except briefly in the canteen. She had been going to ask about the concert but he had been in a hurry. Perhaps he was coming now to tell her about it?

She went to the door and opened it, and blinked.

'Zach?'

'Can I come in?'

'Why?'

It was unwelcoming. She hadn't meant to sound so abrupt, but she felt invaded by him. He unsettled her, and the thought of him in her modest little home unsettled her even worse.

His smile was rueful. 'This isn't a come-on, Jill. I wanted to talk to you about something.'

'Work?'

'No. Not work.'

'What then?'

He rammed a hand through his hair, tumbling the black strands over his forehead in an unruly fashion that made him look wild and sexy and dangerous. She could picture him standing in the rigging, staring out over a storm-tossed sea, a loose white shirt billowing around his powerful chest—

She sighed. What was it about him that made her think of pirates and romance and hot, lusty nights? Especially as she didn't know the first darned thing about hot, lusty nights—

'There's something I think you should know,' he said softly, yanking her mind back to the present day and her doorstep.

'Oh.' Something she should know? How odd. 'You'd better come in, then,' she murmured. She moved back to allow him in, then closed the door and led him through to the kitchen. 'I've got a cup of tea—would you like one?'

'Thanks.'

She filled a mug and handed it to him, then led him outside to her bench. It was a mistake. It was a narrow bench—hardly wide enough for two—and his thigh pressed against hers, radiating heat most disturbingly. She tried to ignore it.

'So, what was it you wanted to tell me?' she asked, puzzled.

He looked uncomfortable. 'I gather you didn't go to the concert with Gordon.'

Her brow creased slightly. 'No. He took his mother. He only had two tickets, and apparently she wanted to go.'

'In which case,' Zach said carefully, 'she was disappointed. Unless, that is, his mother is a twenty-five-year-old lab technician called Maria Skeet.'

Jill felt her blood run cold. 'What?' she whispered. 'What makes you say that?'

'Ryan O'Connor was there—the A and E junior consultant? His late wife's sister was performing. He was sitting behind them.'

Jill shook her head vehemently. 'No. He must have been mistaken—'

'He wasn't mistaken. When Maria found out he was a widower she made it quite clear she wouldn't mind taking over his wife's job. He knows her very well. He also knows Gordon, apparently.' He laid a hand over hers. 'I'm sorry, Jill. I thought you should know, if you didn't already.'

Jill pulled her hand away and stood up, pacing round the small garden. 'There must be an explanation. Perhaps his mother wasn't well at the last minute and he bumped into Maria at the concert hall—perhaps they were just both on their own, sitting together for company.'

'Holding hands?'

Her head snapped round and she stared at Zach in amazement. 'Holding hands? Now I know you're winding me up. Gordon doesn't hold hands—'

'He does with Maria Skeet.'

She couldn't look at him any more. There was pity in his eyes, pity and anger, and she knew that he was telling her the truth.

She turned away, her arms wrapped round her waist against the pain of betrayal. Not that there was much to betray; they hadn't had a very close relationship, but even so—

'He lied to me. Damn it, Zach, he lied to me! How could he?'

Her voice cracked and she bit her lip and squeezed her eyes tight shut. Seconds later she felt strong arms around her, turning her against a broad, solid chest that smelt vaguely of soap and antiseptic and something masculine that made her feel safe.

She laid her head against that lovely safe chest, and one

of his hands came up and cupped the back of her head and soothed it tenderly.

'I'm sorry, Jilly,' he murmured into her hair. 'I thought you ought to know.'

'How dare he?' she whispered. 'How dare he do that to me?'

The hand soothed again, the other arm hugging her even closer against that wonderfully safe chest. Illusion, she thought, was a marvellous thing. There was nothing safe about Zach's chest, nothing at all. It was like standing on the edge of a crumbling cliff top and feeling safe because she was next to a huge rock—also on the cliff and likely to take her over the edge with it!

She stepped back out of his arms and went back to the bench. 'Damn him. I thought we had more than that.'

Zach rejoined her, his arm along the back of the seat just inches from her shoulders. 'How long's your affair been going on?' he asked quietly.

'Affair?' Jill shook her head. 'We weren't having an affair. We didn't have that sort of relationship.'

Zach looked at her in amazement. 'What? How long had you been going out together?'

She shrugged. 'Two or three months.'

'Months? Two or three *months*? Dear God, are you both dead?'

Jill glared at him. 'Not everybody is a raving sex maniac,' she said coldly, trying to ignore the feel of his leg against hers.

He laughed softly, surprise still in his voice. 'Clearly. Nevertheless, normal healthy adults in an established relationship usually do have a physical element to that relationship.'

Jill looked away. 'We did. He used to kiss me goodnight.'

She felt a firm, strong finger curl round her chin and turn her face gently back to him. 'Show me,' he murmured, his breath warm and soft against her lips. 'Show me how he kissed you.'

Her heart jolted under her ribs. She couldn't. She'd have to be crazy to kiss him. . .! After an endless hesitation, she leant forwards and placed her lips against his, just for a moment, then moved away.

'That's it?'

Her eyes were locked with his, fascinated by the change of light in their startling blue depths.

'Yes,' she whispered.

'Not like this?'

His head moved, just a fraction, and his mouth touched hers, soft and coaxing—his lips warm, dry, parting to nibble hers. She felt the velvet sweep of his tongue against her lips, then his hands came up to cup her face, steadying it.

'Give me your mouth,' he ordered gruffly, and fire danced along her veins, leaving her weak with longing.

Her lips parted of their own accord and his tongue traced the sharp, clean line of her teeth, dipping then to explore deeper. He shifted his head slightly and she felt her tongue drawn into his mouth, suckled until she could have cried out. He released it, but it was bold now and she explored the secrets of his mouth without inhibition.

He groaned and took over again, delving deep in her secret places, making the blood race in her veins and her heart pound with a need she hadn't known she could feel.

Then he lifted his head.

'That's how *I'd* kiss you goodnight, Jilly,' he murmured.

Then he was gone, striding swiftly out of her house, the front door slamming gently behind him.

For a long time she didn't move. She couldn't. Her legs

were like jelly, and her body throbbed and ached with a passion newly born and left unslaked.

'Damn you,' she whispered, and she wasn't sure if she was talking about Gordon or Zach, or even if it mattered any more. . .

Damn, but she was gorgeous. Beautiful, spirited and elusive. That, more than anything, piqued his interest.

Zach was used to turning women away—kindly, gently, but nevertheless saying no. They just seemed drawn to him like iron filings to a magnet, and from an early age he had had to learn how to deal with it. His mother said it was his natural charm and come-to-bed eyes that everybody misinterpreted. Whatever, Zach personally thought it was rather a pain. Even the old ladies expected him to flirt with them.

Only Jill glared at him with eyes shooting sparks and that go-to-hell look that made his heart beat faster and his body leap to life.

Zach loved a challenge, though, and if that kiss was anything to go by Jill was a challenge worth taking on. And right now, he thought with a slow smile, she needed a friend.

Perhaps he'd cool the conversation down and try and sneak up on her blind side. Maybe that was the way to get close to the enigmatic Sister Craig. . .

CHAPTER TWO

JILL wasn't sure that she wanted to face Zach the following morning. She didn't know if she could look him in the eye after that kiss — which, incidentally, had kept her awake most of the night.

However, it wasn't a problem. Zach was in Theatre operating, and Jill was busy enough on the ward not to worry. They had had a couple of new admissions overnight — an elderly lady who had had a heavy fall and sustained a fracture of her hip and was now waiting for a replacement, and a young man who had come off his motorbike and hit a tree, thus remodelling his legs. He had been up to Theatre in the night for reduction of the fractures under anaesthetic, and was now in traction and suffering serious self-pity.

Jill was just getting ready to kill him when Zach appeared at her side.

'Hi, there,' he said to the young man and, tugging the curtains round, he peeled off the bedclothes and examined his handiwork. 'Looks good. How does it feel?'

'Awful,' he whimpered. 'I didn't know things could hurt so much.'

Zach snorted. 'Well, just thank your lucky stars you can feel the pain. Your pillion passenger's still unconscious.'

Jill met Zach's eyes and her brows twitched together in a question. He pulled the covers back, told the lad to lie still and not fidget about and he would be on the mend all the sooner, and led Jill out of the cubicle and to the ward office.

'Daft kid's done it before, apparently, but without hurting himself. He was riding a 750 cc bike without a proper licence, and the police want to speak to him as soon as we say he's ready. His friend on the back has head injuries from hitting the tree.'

'Oh, dear God. Will he be all right?'

Zach shrugged. 'Who knows? Brain scan and function tests are promising, but he's still out for the count. He's got a couple of fractures but nothing nasty, so we've imobilised them and we're leaving him alone for now. Ryan reckons he was lucky to have made it to hospital, the state his crash helmet was in.'

Ryan. The man who had seen Gordon with that girl— what was her name? Maria something? Damn him.

'Ouch. Did I say something? You're scowling.'

She looked at Zach, and the gentle, teasing light was back in his eyes and did strange things to her legs. She forced a smile.

'Sorry. I wasn't scowling at you.'

'Gordon.' It was said flatly, without any particular emphasis, and yet Jill knew that he was angry.

She just laughed, a shaky little effort without much humour.

'Sorry. It just makes me so mad. Doesn't anybody believe in fidelity any more?'

'I do.'

'You?' This time the laugh was genuine, and full of amusement. 'Zach, don't be silly. You're a flirt—the nineties' answer to Casanova. You couldn't possibly take a relationship seriously!'

The laughter faded from his eyes, and he reached out and cupped her cheek. 'You could always try me,' he said softly.

She slapped his hand away laughingly, confused by the

tingle in her spine and the way her mouth seemed to want to soften in readiness for his kiss.

'Idiot,' she scolded. 'Anyway, I'm off men. They're all bad news.'

'How about friends?'

She looked up into those gorgeous eyes. 'Friends?' she said as evenly as she could manage.

'Mmm. I could do with a friend—someone to walk the dog with occasionally; someone to look at the barn and tell me I'm making progress.'

'Barn?'

'I'm converting a barn—old, timber-framed job. A bit of moral support would go a long way.'

What was he asking her? She wasn't sure, but she didn't have to wait long. He tipped his head to one side and grinned encouragingly. 'How about this evening, straight after work? You could see the barn, say, "Ooh, ah, such progress!", and we could walk the dog and have a bite to eat and I could run you home.'

The smile was hard to suppress. She reminded herself that he was an inveterate flirt. 'I'm off men.'

'I'm a friend—remember?'

She snorted inelegantly. 'That's not what it felt like last night,' she said, and could have kicked herself for bringing the subject up.

'That was just for demonstration purposes. If I promise to keep my hands to myself, will you come?'

She chewed her lip, conscious of the silliness of going out with him—for all sorts of reasons.

'I can't,' she told him. 'Think of our names. Zach and Jill. Awful. "Zach and Jill went up the hill to fetch a pail of water." Dreadful.'

'How about "Jill and Zach were in the sack, having fun again"?'

'"Zach fell down and broke his crown, and Jill laughed like a drain."'

'That's not nice.'

'It isn't, is it? Anyway, it won't happen. The answer's no. I'm sorry.'

She went out into the ward and he followed her. 'Just because of the names?'

'Of course not. Because of everything. Because you're a man. Because you're a flirt. Because I hate men.'

'You didn't hate me last night,' he said softly, for her ears alone.

She blushed and turned. 'Zach, please. Don't push it.'

He held his hands up, palms towards her in a gesture of submission. 'I'm sorry, I'm sorry—but you have to admit it was a hell of a kiss.'

'I don't have to admit any such thing,' she said primly, but he just chuckled.

'You don't need to,' he told her. 'Your body admitted it for you last night.'

She looked round wildly, but there was no-one within earshot. 'You are the giddy limit,' she snarled under her breath.

He laughed again. '*Touché*. I confess. I'll see you later.' And with a wink and a wave he was gone, leaving her stunned and confused for the second time in twenty four-hours.

She went back to her biker and did his pressure areas, shifting him carefully to make sure that his traction didn't get messed up by him sliding down the bed at all, and he was a pathetic mixture of gratitude and embarrassment. At least he wasn't flirting, though. One in a day was enough.

She went down to the canteen for a late lunch at three and, to her dismay, Gordon came in a moment later and strolled over to join her, looking for all the world as if nothing was wrong or different.

Jill had slow-burning fuses, but this one had had twenty-four hours to reach the powder-keg. It arrived at its destination just as Gordon was about to pull out the chair opposite her.

'How's Maria?' she asked sweetly.

For a moment she thought that he was going to drop the coffee and run but then he hesitated, dropped the chair instead and forced himself to meet her eyes.

'You've heard. That's a pity. I wanted to tell you person-ally. Maria and I will be getting married—'

'Good,' she said clearly—clearly enough for everyone in the room to hear. 'You deserve each other. I hope you'll both be very happy peering down microscopes at smears of human excrement—'

And without another word she stood up, chucked the remains of her coffee all over him and stalked out, leaving Gordon standing dripping with coffee and indignation and surrounded by colleagues with their jaws hanging.

She made it to the ladies' loo before the tears came, and she allowed herself a few moments of complete self-indulgence before washing her face in cold water, scrubbing it dry with a paper towel and standing back to study the mess. Her eyes were swollen and red-rimmed, their grey depths bloodshot and rainwashed, her cheeks were blotchy and her hair needed to be taken down and brushed before being put up again.

Tough. So she looked a wreck.

She yanked the door open and marched up the corridor, ignoring the strange looks she got from the visitors who were filing up the hospital corridors in search of their loved ones.

Mary O'Brien took one look at her as she walked onto

the ward and shoved her into the ward office and sat her down. 'Good gracious, child, whatever's happened to you?'

'Gordon's getting married,' she said without preamble. 'I just embarrassed him in the canteen. It was awful.'

Mary smiled. She actually smiled! 'He was a dreadful man for you, sweetheart. Not at all the right sort, and I'm sure you didn't embarrass him any more than he deserved.'

Jill closed her eyes and sighed. 'I threw my coffee over him.'

Mary's laughter wouldn't be contained, but after a moment she sobered and patted Jill's hand. 'I still say he deserved it. Why don't you go home? You look a fright, girl; you'll terrify the patients. They'll all think they're dying and you daren't tell them.'

Jill laughed, as she was meant to, and nodded. 'Do you mind? I feel pretty rotten. My head hurts and I want to go and yank some weeds up—I'll pretend they're Gordon's hair as I pull them out.'

'Ouch!' Mary chuckled and patted her hand. 'Go on, then, lass; take yourself on home and attack your weeds. I'm just about to do the rotas—I'll get my own back on you.'

'I'm sure,' Jill said drily. 'Thanks.'

She headed home and spent a highly gratifying half-hour murdering the unsuspecting weeds, then went in and ran herself a bath and slid into it with a sigh. She unwound her hair, slithered under the water and lay swishing her head from side to side and letting the blonde strands curl around her shoulders like Medusa's snakes. It was wonderfully relaxing—until she thought that she ought to come out of the water and work out what that awful pounding noise was.

She sat up, water streaming off her in all directions, to hear Zach's voice yelling in the distance.

'Hang on, I'm coming,' she yelled back and scrambled out of the bath, wrapping herself in a huge towel as she ran barefoot up the hall. She yanked the door open, shoving streaming hair out of her eyes, and glared at him. 'Are you trying to break the door down or something?' she demanded.

He stepped back a little. 'Sorry. Are you all right?'

She blinked in astonishment. 'Of course I'm all right. I was in the bath,' she said unnecessarily, and followed the direction of Zach's eyes to the pool of water forming at her feet.

'So I see,' he murmured. He looked relieved. She stood back to let him in and closed the door behind him.

'What did you want?' she asked, not altogether pleased at having been hauled out of her bath to deal with him.

He shoved a hand through his hair. He seemed to do it whenever things got tricky, she'd noticed. 'Mary said you were upset,' he confessed. 'When you didn't answer the door—well, my mind just started working overtime.'

'You didn't think—oh, Lord, you did. Zach.' She smiled reassuringly. 'I wouldn't do anything daft—not over Gordon, at least. He isn't worth it.'

His mouth crooked into a grin. 'I gather you made a scene in the canteen.'

'Just a touch.' She told him what had happened, and he laughed.

'That wasn't kind.'

'It wasn't meant to be,' she retorted, 'but I tell you what, it was satisfying!'

'So.' He looked down at his foot, his toe playing idly with the edge of the doormat. 'If you and Gordon are officially washed up, how about that walk with the dog?'

She twisted her hair up and squashed the water out of it, eyeing him with her head on one side. She was suddenly very, very tempted. 'Do you really have a dog? A real one?'

He laughed, a proper belly laugh. 'Oh, yes,' he said finally. 'He's real, all right. You'll have to meet him.'

'Can you give me fifteen minutes?'

He sobered slightly, studying her searchingly. 'Sure.'

'Good.' She flashed him a smile. 'Make yourself at home in the kitchen; I'll be as quick as I can.'

She went like the wind, but it still took her twenty minutes because of the terrible tangles she'd got in her hair swirling it in the bath. She pulled on clean jeans and a sweater, and lightweight walking boots, and went out into the kitchen. He was outside, on her bench, his head tipped back and his eyes shut, dozing. She kicked his ankle gently and he woke with a start.

'Sorry. Long night. Are you ready?'

'No, I just woke you for devilment,' she teased. 'Yes, I'm ready. Shall we go?'

'Sounds good to me.' He hauled himself to his feet and stretched, his shirt pulling up out of his waistband and giving her a glimpse of lean, hard abdomen that did nothing for her equilibrium.

They went in his car because he said that he wanted her to be able to enjoy the drive, and she wouldn't if she was trying to follow him. It was a lovely drive, through winding lanes and over the gently rolling countryside, and then—at the brow of what passed for a hill—he pointed.

'There it is.' She followed the line of his finger, and on the little rise opposite just a few hundred yards away she saw a black weatherboarded barn, sheltered on two sides by trees, with a field in front and a little track running up towards it along the edge of the field. 'It's got stunning views from this side,' Zach told her. 'It's not big, but I don't need anything huge. It'll be wonderful, though—one day.' He laughed ruefully. 'If I ever get it finished.'

The last part of the drive took only a couple of minutes, down to the valley floor and along the track that led up to the barn. They parked round behind it, beside the edge of the woodland, and as Zach opened the car door a cacophony of noise hit them like a wall. He turned off the engine and ambled over to the barn, opening the door. A huge black thing hurled itself out of the door and flattened him then, realising that Jill was there, swerved and headed for her.

'Scud, no!' Zach yelled, and the avalanche of fur came to a slithering halt at her feet, huge pink tongue lolling and tail thrashing like a crocodile's.

'Hello, boy,' she said cautiously. 'Sit, there's a good dog.'

He wuffed cheerfully at her and sat, rudder sweeping the ground with enthusiasm. 'What did you say his name was?' she asked, unsure if she had heard Zach right.

'Scud—like the missiles?'

'How appropriate.' She looked at Zach, still sprawled on the grass by the door, and she started to chuckle. 'Are you a wicked dog?' she said to Scud, and he grinned, tongue lolling his agreement. She laughed till her sides ached, and the dog sat and wuffed at her for attention and Zach sat there on the grass by the door, arms extended behind him, laughing with her.

'He's a monster—whatever is he?'

'A flat-coated retriever. I don't think he's meant to be quite this big, though. Is he real enough for you?'

She grinned and ruffled his ears, and he swiped her wrist with his tongue and grinned back. 'Just about. Oh, he's lovely.'

'He is—a regular sweetheart, except for a regrettable tendency to sneak onto my bed in the middle of the night. He's my sister's dog, actually, but with the problems with the baby she asked me if I'd have him. He's not really any trouble.'

He'd gone off now, sniffing amongst the long grass beside the track and looking for likely clumps of grass to cock his leg against. Jill chuckled. 'I can see why you laughed when I asked if you had a real dog. He couldn't be much more real.'

'No.' Zach's voice was dry, and he stood up and dusted himself off. 'Any more real and he'd have a government health warning stamped on him. Come on in.'

He held his hand out towards the door in a gesture of welcome, and Jill walked past him into the interior of the barn.

'Oh, my goodness, it's a building site.'

He laughed humourlessly. 'Just a bit. Home, sweet home, eh? Oh, well, I expect I'll get there in the end. I have a tame builder who helps me out.'

She peered round the vast timber cavern, taking in the magnificent beams, the piles of timber and bricks and plasterboard and the beginnings of studwork starting to take shape, created out of more old beams—presumably from another building now demolished.

She saw little traces of domesticity in the midst of the confusion—the divan bed in one corner, an old sheet hanging from a washing-line around another corner acting like a screen, a kitchen table, fridge and microwave in what was presumably going to be the kitchen, a washing-machine with a clothes airer standing on top of it, draped with underwear and shirts—chaos.

She turned to him and smiled faintly. 'I can see why you need a cheerleader.'

He chuckled. 'Bit daunting, isn't it? I was lucky to find a barn with so much already done. The previous owners started well but their marriage foundered.'

'I'm not surprised,' Jill said frankly.

'Not because of the barn,' he said with a grin. 'The chap went off with the woman in the cottage over there.' He pointed towards a pink cottage they could see through the huge glass panel in the centre of the wall.

Jill was more interested in the wonderful window than in what she could see through it. Obviously positioned where the massive old barn doors had once been, it ran from floor to roof level—divided into manageable sections by huge beams that criss-crossed the space. In the centre of the lower section was a pair of French doors leading out onto what she supposed would be a patio at some point in the far distant future, and beyond the patio area— past the pink cottage and into the distance—was the most spectacular view of gently rolling fields dotted with houses and farms.

'Oh, wow, I could look at that all day,' she said with a sigh. 'I can see why you bought it!'

'I'm glad you like it,' he murmured. 'I like to think Grannie would have approved. It was her money that bought it.' He laughed softly. 'My only regret is that she didn't live to see it but if she had we wouldn't be here anyway, so it's all rather illogical. At least I know I'm not the only one to see the charm in it—even if it does need about four million man hours to turn it into a home!'

Jill turned and looked at the interior again. 'Explain it to me,' she asked. 'What's going where?'

So he pointed out the sitting-room, the kitchen area, the hallway which was by the wonderful glass wall and would extend up an open staircase to a galleried landing around the window, the utility room and cloakroom which explained the sheet draped round the corner—'my bath-room,' he elaborated, showing her the loo and shower cubicle behind the primitive screen—and then the upstairs rooms with bathrooms he indicated by waving at the almost non-existent ceiling.

'And that's it,' he said.

'Just like that.'

He laughed. 'It's so easy to say, isn't it? Oh, well, one day. Right, give me ten seconds to change out of this gear and we'll walk the dog.'

He went over to the 'bedroom' corner and without pre-amble or modesty he stripped off his shirt and trousers and tugged on a pair of jeans and an old sweater. Jill tried not to look—she really did try, but one glimpse of that sleek, well-muscled torso and she was lost. And his legs—oh, Lord, she wanted to touch them; to see if the hair scattered over those long, lean thighs was soft to the touch or if it would feel rough against her hand—

She dragged in a shaky breath and headed for the door. 'I'm going to have a look outside,' she said hurriedly, and shot out into the open air, dragging in a quick lungful of it and sagging against the wall. What on earth was she doing here? He was too relaxed, too casual. There were no boundaries or inhibitions; nothing to stop her from falling headlong into deep, deep trouble.

And she was already in trouble. She knew that. She'd never felt this way about anyone, never been moved to these kinds of urges and desires by another man.

So why this one? Why choose the man she had described as the nineties' answer to Casanova?

'Idiot,' she muttered.

Something warm and wet and disgusting wrapped itself round her hand, and she yanked it up and gave a little shriek.

'Scud!' she admonished. 'Did you lick me?'

He grinned, his liquid brown eyes sparkling with intelligence and merriment. For something so large, she thought, he moved with enormous stealth. She hadn't heard him come up to her at all, but it wasn't surprising. She couldn't hear a great deal over the pounding of her heart.

She heard Zach, though, or perhaps her body just sensed him as he came out of the door behind her.

'Are you all right? I heard you yell.'

'Scud sneaked up on me and licked me. It was gross.'

He chuckled. 'You want to try one of his wake-up calls.'

No, I don't, she thought, because you'd be there and that could only mean one thing—

'All set?'

She nodded. 'Yes. Where are we going?'

'Through the wood. Scud likes to chase the rabbits. He's not outstandingly successful, so I let him do it.'

They set off through the little wood, and Jill could see the leaves of bluebells starting to push up into the dappled light. It was going to be beautiful once all the leaves were out on the trees and the bluebells were in flower. Scud was foraging around in the undergrowth looking for fascinating scents, and the birds were calling to each other in the branches overhead. There were no other sounds apart from their footsteps and the distant hum of a tractor.

'It's so peaceful,' she murmured.

'It is, isn't it? I come in here whenever I can—which explains why I don't get a great deal done, of course.'

They shared a smile of understanding, and Jill's heart leapt against her ribs. What had happened to the teasing flirt? He was just a normal man now, sharing her love of the countryside, looking relaxed and at home in his casual clothes and suddenly much more and much less of a threat.

Less because he seemed suddenly a much more solid

and deep-thinking person than she had given him credit for, and more because that made him all the more attractive and thus infinitely more dangerous because she knew that it was just an illusion.

He stopped walking and turned towards her, a question in his eyes. Her lips felt suddenly dry. Knowing what it would do to him, unable to stop herself, she flicked the tip of her tongue out to moisten them.

He groaned softly and then she was in his arms, her chest pressed up against his, their legs tangling, one of his big, solid hands cupping the back of her head to steady it as his mouth came down on hers without hesitation.

She went up in flames. There was no doubt, no holding back, no thought at all. Just need, pure and simple, and Zach filling that need with lips and tongue and hands, dragging her harder against his body so that she could feel his instant and devastating response.

After an age he lifted his head and tucked her head under his chin, his hand stroking her hair with long, soothing strokes as he held her against his pounding heart.

At least she thought it was his. It could just as easily have been hers, they were so close together.

He said nothing. She was grateful for that. There didn't seem to be anything sensible to say; nothing that wouldn't spoil the moment.

After a few minutes he turned, wrapping his arm round her shoulders, and started walking on again through the wood. She could hear Scud crashing about in the undergrowth, and the beat of her heart, and the soft scrunch of leaves beneath their feet.

She wanted him.

It was incredible. She'd never wanted to be with someone—to hold them, to touch them—as she wanted to be with Zach.

They didn't speak again all the way back to the barn. She wondered what he would say when he did speak. There was only one thing on their minds, and to speak about it seemed unthinkable. If they acknowledged it, put it into words, it would grow and engulf them and there would be no getting away.

There was no getting away.

They went into the barn through the back door, as before, and he turned to her and met her eyes for the first time. The raw, blazing need etched on his face shocked her; it was such an exact echo of her own.

'This isn't finished, Jilly,' he warned softly.

Her breath jammed in her throat. 'I know,' she replied, and her voice was tight and strained.

'Do you want me to take you home?'

He was giving her a way out, but suddenly she didn't want it.

'No,' she breathed. Then, 'No,' a little more strongly, with more conviction.

'Good.' He said nothing else, just held out his hand and led her to the bed in the corner. Then he stripped down to his briefs and reached for the hem of her sweater, pulling it up over her head.

She wasn't wearing a bra. Her figure wasn't very full and she hardly needed one, but now, suddenly, she wished she had bothered because she felt unbearably naked and vulnerable. What if he found her small breasts unappealing?

She needn't have worried. Zach's breath jerked in in a rush, and then slowly, hesitantly, he reached out to cup the slight fullness. His hand was trembling, she noticed in surprise. Then his slightly rough palm cupped her breast and she stopped thinking completely and just gave herself over to sensation.

His thumb grazed her nipple, making it peak and pucker for him, and he bent his head and touched it with his tongue, blowing on it to make it stand up even more. The other one ached, and as if he knew he switched his attention to it and licked it, too, bringing it to instant attention.

His hand slid down, away from her breasts, and the other one joined it at the stud on her jeans, dispensing with stud and zip in seconds. She kicked her shoes off and he pushed her jeans over her hips, his hands following the contours round to cup her bottom and draw her up against him.

His chest was smooth and sleek, the skin like satin drawn taut over the supple muscles beneath. Between his flat, copper nipples there was a light dusting of hair that tantalised her soft, tender skin as he chafed against her. He pushed her jeans down and she stepped out of them, hanging onto his shoulders for support, and then his arms were round her and his mouth was on hers and there was no more hesitation, no distractions, no barriers. Their underwear was gone, swept aside by his impatient hands, and after a fumbling moment punctuated by a muttered curse he was lying over her on the bed, one large, bony knee between hers, nudging her thighs apart to receive him.

Then he was there, inside her, filling her, easing the terrible need and yet driving it still higher.

With a little cry she bucked against him and he made a low, guttural sound in his throat and took her mouth in a deep, penetrating kiss that matched the urgent thrusting of his body as it arched over hers.

The need grew, swamping her, and then suddenly her body exploded in flames, tongues of ecstasy licking along her limbs until the heat receded, leaving her limp in his arms. She was conscious of nothing but the harsh sound of his breathing in her ear, the pounding of his body on hers and the sudden stiffening as she felt the pulsing of his release deep within her.

A great groan was torn from his chest, then he sagged against her, sweat breaking out on his skin. She smoothed it away with hands that shook in the aftermath of their love-making.

After an age his breathing steadied and he lifted his head and stared down at her. 'OK?' he murmured softly.

She nodded. She didn't really feel OK. She felt as if her world had been picked up and hurled across the universe; tilted on its axis; drenched in the golden light of a different, somehow more glorious sun. OK didn't begin to touch it.

'Wonderful,' she whispered, and she reached up and touched his cheek with fingers that shook at the beauty of what he had given her.

He swallowed hard and dropped his head back into the curve of her shoulder. 'Heavy,' he mumbled after a moment, and shifted slightly so that he was lying half beside her, half on her still. He couldn't go any further because her legs were wrapped tightly round him, holding him locked within her, so he rolled her carefully to her side and drew her back into his arms.

She snuggled closer, unwilling to relinquish any of the wonderful contact, and within seconds she was asleep.

Zach lay awake, his hands stroking the soft, fine skin of her shoulders. Her legs were locked around his waist, the smooth length of her thigh against his side, warm and heavy and possessive.

His hip was digging into her other leg and he tried to move a little but her legs tightened convulsively, holding him intimately against her vulnerable softness. He smiled. Even in her sleep she wanted him.

He eased away a fraction, just enough to deal with the

condom he had remembered to use at the very last second, and then settled down again with her head on his shoulder, allowing himself the luxury of studying her.

Skin like pale gold, her blonde hair tangled on the pillow and across his chest, her darker lashes fanned against her cheeks with the innocence of a child—she was beautiful. He could feel the soft press of her small breasts against his side, so pert and perfect. He felt his body stir and thought of waking her to make love again, but she looked tired. There would be time later.

Restless, filled with a wonderful energy now, he eased himself away from her and covered her, then showered and dressed quickly before making a cup of coffee and settling down to study the plans for the next phase of work on the barn. Scud whined at the door and he let him in, scolding him in an undertone when he headed for the bed and calling him back to his side.

'Stay here, boy,' he ordered, and Scud dropped at his feet with a groan and lay with paws outstretched, his massive head resting on them, watching Zach out of one eye.

Zach stared at the plans and saw Jilly, her body naked, stretched out waiting for him, arching towards him eagerly. Damn, he wanted her again. She had felt so good beneath him—so warm, so giving, so incredibly right. No one had ever felt so right.

Not that there'd been that many. He'd always been very fussy, and sex for its own sake had never appealed. Even so, with the few serious affairs he had had, he'd never felt the overwhelming surge of tenderness and nurturing he'd felt with this very special woman.

He glanced over at her and groaned. She had shifted, throwing back the quilt, and her breasts were pointing pertly at him, beckoning. He shut his eyes, counted to ten and forced his attention back to the plans.

CHAPTER THREE

JILL was being crushed—crushed by something warm and wet and very heavy, slathering across her face.

A voice roared in the distance and the weight was gone. She cautiously opened an eye, then shut it again hurriedly.

Oh, Lord, she was in Zach's bed. It hadn't been a dream, and the ghastly heavy wet thing was Scud's wake-up call.

She hadn't intended to be here for that.

For any of it.

Oh, hell.

She lay motionless, pretending to be asleep still, and remembered. It had been wonderful, the most incredible experience of her adult life, and she didn't know how to open her eyes and look at him because he was a total stranger. She had known him for two short weeks, and in that time she had done her best to avoid him.

Had it been special for him? Probably not. Casanovas were probably used to spectacular firework displays every time they went to bed with anyone. Oh, well, at least one spin-off from his promiscuous lifestyle was that he had remembered to take precautions, because she sure as eggs had forgotten all about it.

Damn. How could she have just fallen into bed with him when he crooked his little finger? How weak. How spineless and pathetic.

How desperate.

She rolled her face into the pillow and groaned softly. Damn her stupidity. Now she was just another notch on

44

his bedpost, just another conquest to add to the list of thousands. Humilation turned her skin crimson.

She felt the side of the bed dip, and a warm, damp flannel was wiped carefully over her face. 'I'm sorry about Scud,' Zach murmured.

'Forget it,' she mumbled. The dog was the least of her worries.

'Jilly?' His fingers cupped her chin and turned it towards him, but she refused to open her eyes. 'Damn,' he said quietly, and then his weight was gone from the edge of the bed and she was alone again.

'I'll be outside,' he told her. 'Feel free to use the shower. There's a clean towel on the end of the bed. Scud, come on.'

She heard the soft click of the door, rolled onto her back and stared up into the rafters overhead. It was gloomy now, and a table lamp cast a soft, eerie light over the inside of the barn. It was dusk outside so she imagined that it must be between seven and eight. She threw back the bedclothes, grabbed her scattered clothes and the towel and ducked behind the sheet in the corner.

The shower tray was wet and so was the bathmat, so Jill assumed that Zach must have already showered. Had she been so heavily asleep that she hadn't noticed him leave the bed? They had been totally entangled. How had he managed to slip away like that?

Her cheeks heated again at the memory, and she turned the shower temperature down to cool and stepped under the stinging spray. It was a power shower, the force amazing, and it took her breath away for a moment. That— and the knowlege that Zach was waiting outside for a conversation she was definitely not looking forward to.

She dried and dressed quickly and went outside to face him. He was sitting on a fallen log with the dog at his feet, staring out over his valley, and he looked strained in the dusky light.

'Better now?' he said quietly.

She nodded. At least she was dressed and standing up. She felt infinitely less vulnerable than she had still lying in the tangle of his sheets, her body warm from their loving.

He searched her face, then looked away with a sigh. He was holding a twig in his hand and she could see now that he was shredding it systematically, peeling the bark and stripping the wood away layer by layer.

He tossed it on the ground finally and looked back at her. 'We shouldn't have done that.'

She was amazed. Whatever response she had expected, it hadn't been that. Oh, she agreed, wholeheartedly, but she was still amazed.

'Why?' she asked, unable to help herself.

'Because you can't look me in the eye. Because you regret it. Because you were impulsive and free and foolish for once in your well-ordered life, and now you regret the impulse that allowed you to abandon your inhibitions and play.'

'I don't know you,' she told him, in justification. 'We're almost strangers. Things like that should happen in the context of a relationship, and the only relationship we have is that of colleagues.'

'You didn't feel like a colleague in there a little while ago.'

Her breath caught and fire flooded her cheeks. 'Nevertheless, I am. That's all I am.'

He studied her in silence for a moment, then said, 'Why do I get the feeling that if we weren't colleagues we wouldn't be having this conversation—because you would just run off and never see me again? It's only because we have to work together that you're forced to stand there and talk to me and thrash this out, since we both know there's no way we can walk onto that ward in the morning and face each other after what's happened without discussing it, and you can't do what you really want to do and run away.'

The very thought of seeing him again in the morning made her blood run cold. The embarrassment would be excruciating.

She looked down at her feet, scuffing a stone with her toe. 'I'm sorry. You're right, I do regret it. It should never have happened.'

'So why did you let it?'

She shrugged, lost in her confusion and a welter of unfamiliar emotions. She struggled for a defence that would shield her vulnerability, and came up with a weak and implausible lie. 'I don't know. Gordon, maybe? I was so angry with him—hurt. Perhaps it was just a reaction.'

He was silent for so long that she looked up at him, and was stunned at the anger blazing in his eyes. 'You used me as an *aspirin*?' he said with deadly emphasis, and she realised that she'd taken her own defence too far. 'Damn you, Jill. How dare you use me like that? I should have realised a woman like you couldn't do anything that spontaneous without a motive!'

He jackknifed to his feet and strode away to the car, yanking open the passenger door. 'Get in,' he said abruptly. 'I'll take you home. I need some sleep; I don't have time for this.'

Shocked by the change in him and stunned by the complete absence of any kindness or affection after all that had transpired and yet unable to undo the words that had caused the rift, she stumbled silently to the car and got in, slamming the door shut and turning her face to stare out of the window.

The engine roared to life, and with a barked command to the dog to 'Stay!', Zach spun the wheel and sent the car hurtling down the track at terrifying speed.

They skidded onto the road at the bottom, fishtailed through a bend and then finally he settled down and drove properly for the last few miles to the hospital. He pulled up outside her flat without a word and she got out in silence and walked up the path to the door, her trembling legs barely able to carry her. Whatever she'd said there was no need to drive like that! She was terrified, her heart hammering in her chest, and her regret was turned to anger. He was gone before she had the key in the lock, roaring away with scant regard for the speed limit, behaving like the juvenile that he was.

So his ego was dented.

Better that, she thought bitterly, than a broken heart. She opened the door and went through into the dark hallway, shutting the door behind her and going straight into her bedroom. Then she fell over onto the bed, buried her face in the pillow and howled her eyes out.

Zach was stunned. Stunned, hurt, confused and downright angry. How dared she? How the hell could she have done that? He attacked the barn, doing some of the more physical jobs that were outstanding to burn off some of the boiling fury that seemed to fill him. It only worked to a limited extent, though.

By the time he fell into bed Zach was exhausted, his urge to smash things slaked, but his heart was still raw. Had it really meant so little to her? Had that sneaking creep Gordon really meant so much?

He punched the pillow and turned his face into it, only to groan with agonised frustration.

It smelt of her—the wild meadow scent of her shampoo,

the faint hint of some other nameless fragrance that made his gut clench and his undisciplined and undaunted body harden in response.

He swore and threw back the bedclothes, rummaging in a trunk for fresh sheets to banish her from his mind.

He might as well not have bothered.

The night didn't bring Jill much in the way of rest and, because life was like that, the ward in the morning was a mass of little problems requiring Zach's attention right under Jill's nose.

Robert Ryder's team wasn't operating that day, which meant that Zach was not only needed on the ward but very much available.

Not that it affected Jill directly because he hardly spoke more than ten words to her, and all of them were about patients. It was perfect therapy. She spent the day getting crosser and crosser with him; the phenomenal nerve of the man, taking the hump because *she* had used *him*!

Clearly he was so used to doing the using that his ego was devastated when the boot appeared to be on the other foot!

In fact it wasn't, of course, but there was no way she was going to be able to convince him of that. He had decided that she had used him to forget Gordon, and she could tell from the shuttered look on his face that there was no way he would listen to any explanation she might offer.

She wasn't sure that she wanted to offer an explanation, anyway. What could she say? That she had been so overcome by the force of his sexual magnetism that her body had overruled her mind? Not in this lifetime, she thought drily. His ego simply didn't need that sort of boost, and a girl had her pride.

So she soldiered on and ignored him, and he ignored

her, until by the end of the day her nerves were at screaming pitch.

Then Mrs Birkett's husband came in as drunk as a skunk and slipped through the net, and the next thing was he was threatening Jill and Zach was dragging him away from her and the police were coming and it was all very dramatic and fraught.

By the time she had settled the sobbing woman down and increased her pethidine to soothe her pain after all the jostling about, the police had taken Mr Birkett away to charge him with assaulting Jill, causing an affray and all sorts of other legalese which meant that he would be spending the night in the cells and probably coming back full of hate the following day.

She really didn't need it. Mrs Birkett didn't need it either, but she had married the man. Jill hadn't. She went home to her flat, yanked out a few more weeds and wondered how long it would be before she could look at Zach and not want to cry.

The doorbell rang.

'This is getting to be a habit,' she muttered, stomping up the hall with ill grace.

She yanked the door open and a huge bouquet of flowers was thrust into her arms. 'Miss Craig?'

'Yes?'

'Sign here, please.'

She took the pen, scratched her signature on the delivery boy's form and shut the door. Flowers? Who on earth would send her flowers?

Gordon? Hardly, after the way she had behaved.

Zach? Bound to be. He'd probably decided that he'd made her suffer long enough and would suck up to her again.

She took them into the kitchen and put them down on

the draining board, then plucked the little card out of the middle.

'"I've decided to forgive you for the scene in the canteen. You were, after all, provoked. I hope you'll find it in your heart to wish us well. Gordon and Maria."' Well, hell. Gordon and Maria indeed. So he's going to forgive me, is he? Pompous ass.'

She dumped the flowers in the kitchen bin and rubbed the back of her hand over her nose, then sniffed. Damn Zach. She'd been sure they would be from him. He couldn't even get that right.

The doorbell rang again and she scrubbed the tears off her cheeks and almost yanked the door off its hinges.

'You,' she said with an unflattering lack of enthusiasm.

Zach searched her face, then stepped in and pushed the door shut behind himself. 'I owe you an apology.'

She snorted and turned away, marching down the hall to the kitchen. 'You don't say. What for, in particular? Taking advantage of me last night? Accusing me of using you as an aspirin? Treating me like a piece of furniture all day?'

'Basically, yes.'

She spun on her heel. 'Yes? Just like that, yes?'

'I spoke to Mary. Or rather, more accurately, she spoke to me. She asked me what the hell I'd done to you to make you look like last week's spaghetti. I told her, and she hit the roof. She said you didn't have a vindictive bone in your body. She said you weren't in the least upset about Gordon, just about being cheated on, and that no way would you use anybody like that and I had to be off my trolley to think it. She wouldn't say any more. Said I should ask you, but she advised me to apologise first. Coincidentally, she accused me of being blind and ignorant and a lousy judge of character.'

'Wise woman, Mary O'Brien. Well, you've apologised; you can go now.'

'No.'

She glared at him. At least she meant to, but his eyes were full of remorse and his mouth looked so inviting and she knew quite well that if she let him, he'd kiss her.

It all rather took the glare off the glare, and turned it into something much more welcoming and forgiving.

'Oh, damn you,' she whispered, and went into his arms.

He hugged her then let her go, leaning back to look down into her face. 'Forgive me?'

'If I must. I couldn't believe how cold you were, after all that had happened.'

'I know. I couldn't, either, but I couldn't believe you let me make love to you so soon, without any lead-up to speak of. It seemed the only rational explanation for something that seemed so out of character.'

She laughed softly. 'Try sweeping me off my feet for size.'

He grinned. 'I did? Well, how about that?'

She hit him, still hurt after the night before but willing to forgive—if he didn't get too cocky.

He pointed over her shoulder at the bin with the mangled bouquet plonked in it, still tied with a huge and vulgar bow. 'Who are the flowers from?'

She laughed. 'Gordon and Maria, if you please. He says he'll forgive me for the scene in the canteen as it was provoked.'

'Big of him.'

'I thought so.'

They shared a smile.

'So,' he said softly, 'are you going to tell me the reason you got so mad at being cheated? Apart from the obvious, of course. I seem to remember the last time we talked about it you asked if anyone believed in fidelity any more. Was that desperately significant?'

She gave a wry grin. 'Probably. Let's just say I've had my fingers burnt in the past.'

He took her hand and smoothed the fingers with his thumb. 'Poor Jilly. Tell me.'

She lifted her shoulders. 'It's an old story and hardly a new one. I was twenty and totally innocent, and I thought he was wonderful. He was thirty-two, married, two children and a constant stream of mistresses. I think I was somewhere between the girl in the dry cleaners and the waitress in the pub, if I remember correctly from what his wife said the night she caught us together. You see, my replacement was already under way.'

'Poor baby. All those illusions shattered all at once.'

'They were. It was dreadful. I swore I'd never trust another man again.'

'Hence Gordon.'

Her brow puckered. 'What?'

'Gordon,' he said, lounging back against the worktop. 'You obviously thought if you went for someone as terminally unappealing as Gordon, you'd be safe because nobody else would want him. Unfortunately you were wrong. Somebody else did.'

She laughed softly. Damn, he had a way of hitting the nail on the head. 'Am I so transparent?' she asked despairingly.

His smile was comforting. 'Only to me.'

'Because you know all the moves?'

'Because I care about you.'

She laughed, then. 'Liar,' she said cheerfully, but he shook his head.

'I'm not lying, Jilly. Last night was too much too soon,

but that didn't make what happened between us any less than it was.'

She swallowed the lump that suddenly appeared in her throat. 'Damn it, Zach,' she muttered, and he pulled her back into his arms and hugged her.

'Can we start again?' he asked. 'Get to know each other slowly; build up some trust? I think that's something we both have a problem with.'

She stood there in his arms, seething with indecision, wondering if she was about to make the second biggest mistake of her life—the first having been the night before.

'All right,' she said softly. 'But slowly. And, no—well—you know.'

'Making love?'

Even the words sent a dart of desire through her. 'Mmm,' she mumbled incoherently.

'OK.' She lifted her head in surprise and looked at him, and his mouth tipped in a crooked grin. 'It'll kill me, but OK. In fact, it's a good idea. I don't ever want to see you look at me with regret in your eyes again.'

His knuckles brushed her cheek, and as if it was in some way connected to her knees they felt suddenly weak. She wondered why she'd bothered with the stipulation but it was too late now to retract it, even though her traitorous body was all ready to fall at his feet.

'Tea?' she offered, scrabbling for a neutral topic that would give her a moment to get back her equilibrium.

He chuckled. 'The Englishman's answer to everything. No, sweetheart, I won't. I have to go back to walk the dog, and I really must get something done in the house tonight. Anyway, I think we could do with a little breathing space to let things settle down before we push our luck, don't you?'

And with that he kissed her goodnight, not the chaste

sort of kiss she had had from Gordon, nor yet the bone-melting, heart-stopping kiss she had received yesterday, but something in between—a tender caress that left her gently regretful of her hands-off clause but yet not climbing walls. Quite.

Then he was gone, leaving her alone to pull Gordon's flowers out of the bin and arrange them because it was hardly the fault of the flowers that Gordon was such a creep; then she had a bath and went to bed at a reasonable hour. She even managed to sleep, although the dreams were full of the very stuff of her regrettable clause...

She was right about Mr Birkett. He was released from police custody next morning and came straight back in, despite being warned against it, and threatened Jill again.

'I have a right to talk to my wife, and not you or anybody else is going to stop me!' he told her defiantly, and marched into the cubicle where Mrs Birkett was being nursed.

Jill followed him, furious to the point where she lost track of common sense. 'Mr Birkett, I'm sorry but it isn't visiting time at the moment, and the consultant is just coming to do his rounds. I'm going to have to ask you to leave.'

He didn't even bother to look at her. He just went straight up to his wife and sat down, taking her hand in his and leaning forward to talk urgently to her.

'Two minutes,' Jill said. 'Then you go or I call the police.'

'Get stuffed.'

Jill got hold of her temper with difficulty and left the room, going into the office to call Security and warn them that there might be a problem. 'Could you have someone circulating in the area just in case?' she asked.

Then she went quietly back towards Mrs Birkett's little room. They didn't hear her coming, both intent on a low-voiced and grim exchange.

Mrs Birkett was on the verge of tears, and her husband pointed a finger at her and said, 'Say nothing,' in a vicious undertone.

Her eyes widened. 'I haven't,' she said helplessly. 'Oh, Brian, please, let it rest. I've said I'm sorry. I won't try it again.'

'I won't let you go,' he warned. 'Not now, not ever. Is that clear? And if they put me away I'll still get you, one way or the other. I've got friends, Doll. They'll track you down. You won't be safe.'

'And I'm safe now?' she said bitterly. 'Oh, Brian, for God's sake, let me go. I won't say anything. I promise. Just leave me alone.'

'I think it's time to go, Mr Birkett,' Jill said quietly from the doorway. 'I've called Security. They'll escort you from the building.'

He turned on her, his face contorted in a vicious snarl. 'Just who the hell do you think you are, lady?' he said menacingly.

She straightened. 'I'm the nurse in charge of your wife's care, Mr Birkett. It's my duty to ensure that she has a speedy and uneventful recovery, uninhibited by threats and coercion from you or anybody else. If you can't handle that then I suggest you don't come back.'

For such a big man, he moved with surprising speed.

So, fortunately for Jill, did Zach, stepping between them at the last second and twisting Mr Birkett's arm up behind his back and slamming him into the wall without ceremony. The uniformed security guard appeared like the cavalry a second later and joined in, and Jill—shaken but unharmed—went over to Mrs Birkett and hugged her gently.

'It's all right, Dolly. It's OK. You'll be all right.'

'No,' she whispered. 'I won't. Why didn't I die?'

Jill was appalled. There seemed to be nothing she could say, except to promise that he wouldn't be allowed into the hospital again to visit her.

'You can get a restraining order put on him so that he can't come near you.'

She laughed a little wildly. 'You think that would work? Didn't you hear him? He's got friends, Sister. He might not get near me, but he'd find a way to make sure someone did. There's always someone owes him a favour. He'd just call it in and I'd—well, let's just say if I was lucky they'd kill me quickly.'

Jill took her hand and Mrs Birkett gripped it hard. 'Don't do anything about what you heard, please. I've tried for years to escape from him. I almost managed once but he tracked me down at the shelter and he watched me for three months before he got me on my own. It was six weeks before I could go out in public. I don't want to go through that again, believe me.'

'Dolly, he nearly killed you!'

She turned away. 'I slipped,' she said doggedly.

'If you say so.'

'I do. I have to, love. I've got no choice. Just keep me safe as long as you can, eh? That's all you can do.'

Jill patted her hand and left her, going out into the ward to find Zach. He was lounging by the workstation, cradling one hand against his chest and looking sorry for himself.

'What happened to you?' she asked. 'Did Birkett hurt you?'

He gave a wry grin. 'No. A bit of studwork fought back.

Can you have a look at it? That's why I was coming to find you.'

'Sure. Come in the treatment room.' She led him over to the room where they changed dressings and carried out sterile procedures, and told him to sit on the treatment couch. 'Right, let's have a look—ouch!'

His mouth tipped a little. 'Tell me about it. A great lump of oak the size of a sumo wrestler's thigh and about one and a half times my height decided to fight back just as I was pegging it into position. My hand rather got in the way.'

Jill frowned. The whole of the back of his left hand was gloriously coloured and covered in deep grazes, the fingers swollen, and it looked to her as if he might well have at least one fracture. 'Wiggle your fingers,' she ordered.

He obliged. 'There's nothing broken,' he told her mildly. 'I've squashed it and poked it and—ow!'

'You were saying?'

'You're vicious. Look, Jill, I can move it—OK, it's a bit stiff, but it's basically all right. I just need the grazes covered for hygiene.'

Jill met his eyes, his fingers still lying loosely in her hand as it rested against his thigh. 'Go and have an X-ray,' she said firmly.

'No—'

'Yes. Please?'

He grinned. 'Anybody would think you cared about me.'

She snorted, only too conscious of the warmth of his hard thigh under her hand. Care? Oh, yes, and the rest, but he wasn't about to know that. 'Don't get carried away, blue-eyes,' she said laughingly. 'By the way, thanks for rescuing me from Birkett. He's a nasty piece of work. I need to get onto the police about arranging some protection for her from him—a restraining order or something. He's going to kill her if nobody stops him, you know. And he did drop her.'

'She admitted it?' He looked astonished.

Jill gave a rueful grin and shook her head. 'Not in so many words. It's not the first time he's hurt her badly, though. She's only with him because she can't get away. I think he's a cruel, vicious man who gets off on hurting people, and she's the ideal victim—too terrified to do anything to protect herself. She just begs and pleads, and that gives him the kicks he needs.'

'Bastard,' Zach muttered. 'If I had two good hands I'd sort him out myself.'

Jill laughed and retrieved her hand from his lap. 'You and whose army? He's enormous, Zach. He must weigh twice what you do. Now, go and get that checked out in A and E, and come and report back to me.'

'Yes, miss.' He slid off the edge of the desk and pulled her to her feet and into his arms.

'Hey! None of that! You agreed!'

'I agreed not to make love to you. I didn't agree not to touch you or hold you or kiss you—'

'Oops!'

Jill turned her head sharply and caught Mary's wink to Zach as she reversed out of the room. She dropped her head on his chest and groaned. 'That's done it. Of all the places to choose—'

'Your house, later. Or mine. I won't be able to do anything to the barn tonight—how about trying for another walk? If I get out of line you'll only have to wiggle my fingers and I'll co-operate instantly!'

'I don't think that's a good idea—'

'Of course, if you don't feed me I won't be able to eat tonight. I can't open tins with one hand.'

She rolled her eyes and backed away from him, out of his arms.

'Go and have your X-ray, Dr Samuels. We'll discuss this later.'

'If I get them to lie and say I've broken it, will you take pity on me?'

She snorted. 'Don't push your luck, sunbeam. Go on, go and get it checked out. I don't have time to stand here and argue with you. Oh, by the way, Jason Bridger was asking if there was any news on his pillion passenger.'

'Dave? Yes, he's come round. Luckily, he seems all right. He'll be transferred up here for fracture management later today, I think. Check with Neurology—he's their patient at the moment.'

'I will. I'll go and give Jason the good news—and you—'

'Go and have an X-ray,' he mimicked, and saluted with his good hand. 'See you in a tick.'

It was, in fact, more like three quarters of an hour, and he returned with his arm in a back-slab cast and an expression of disgust on his face. 'Two metacarpals,' he grumbled. 'They'll need pinning.'

'Zach!' Jill was instantly concerned. 'Oh, Lord, I didn't think it was that bad—why are you laughing?'

He winked cheerfully. 'Gotcha.'

'What?'

He pulled the backslab off and wiggled his hand. 'I talked the nurses into doing it just to wind you up. I'm fine. No fractures, but I can't operate for a few days, of course, and I've got to go and see the physio—ouch! What was that for?'

Jill glared at him. 'Winding me up. I'll hit you again if you don't stop smiling.'

He tugged her into his arms and kissed her forehead. 'Sorry.'

'You will be. Zach, you can't just keep grabbing me on the ward! People will talk!'

'We're in your office. No one can see us.'

'All the more dangerous—and, anyway, it's Mary O'Brien's office. So, what are you doing now?'

'Ward round?'

She frowned at his hand. 'Can you manage?'

'If you put a dressing on it.'

'OK.'

She took him back into the treatment room, carefully leaving the door open to make him behave, and gently wrapped his hand in non-adherent dressing and bandaged it.

'That's a bit over the top, isn't it? A sticking plaster would have done.'

She glared into those gorgeous blue eyes. 'You complaining again?'

He grinned. ' Of course not. You could always kiss me better.'

'Take a hike. Come on, ward round. You've got patients waiting while you mess about wasting NHS resources on bogus plaster casts.'

He trailed after her, grumbling cheerfully about her lack of compassion and understanding, and she struggled with the stupid grin that kept working its way onto her face. He was still a shocking flirt. She had to remember that. Flirting came to him as easily as breathing. She should keep his attention in perspective, and try and forget what it had felt like to lie in his arms.

That had been a temporary aberration, a momentary lapse in common sense, and she wasn't going to let his charm and flirtation drag her into another such lapse.

No, she wasn't.

Not at all.

Ever.

Mrs Birkett was making slow but steady progress—physically. Her feet were a good colour, her legs were generally less painful and the suture lines looked clean and were healing well.

Her back was still very tender, and there was still a tingling sensation in her left leg and an area of numbness over the skin of her foot but, all in all, she was making a remarkable recovery.

Physically.

Emotionally, she was on a definite downer. Zach decided that she should see a psychologist to see if her self-esteem could be raised to a level where she felt it was justified to fight back at her bully of a husband. Apparently his sister had seen a psychologist and had found it enormously helpful.

Jill was surprised that he held with psychology. A lot of surgeons regarded it as halfway between religion and witchcraft, on a par with acupuncture and aromatherapy in terms of efficacy. Zach, she discovered, believed in both.

'We're so ignorant of the subtleties of our world,' he said to her. 'We blithely destroy our planet with ignorance, upsetting the delicate balance of nature, because we don't have all the answers. As far as I'm concerned, if something works—no matter the reason—that's good enough for me. I like to try and understand, but I don't *have* to know, though. I'm not so arrogant that I think I have to have all the answers. Like I said, whatever works—and psychologists are working more and more with patients after trauma. Ryan often refers patients admitted through A and E.'

His attitude surprised her. She would have had him pegged as the dismissive, not-that-hocus-pocus type of man. Instead, she found that he was open-minded and prepared to be persuaded. It was somewhat of a revelation. Perhaps it was Ryan O'Connor's influence?

She knew the softly spoken Canadian doctor slightly from his visits to the ward, and resolved to pay more attention to him the next time she saw him. He might be able to shed some light on the enigma that Zach was fast becoming. . .

CHAPTER FOUR

IN FACT, the next time Jill saw Ryan was not on the ward at all, but at Zach's barn. It was the weekend, and Zach had managed to persuade her that she would be perfectly safe spending a few hours there in daylight.

'I seem to remember it was daylight before,' she commented drily. 'I don't recall it made a great deal of difference.'

He grinned sheepishly. 'I'll behave, I promise.'

'You said that before, too.'

His smile slipped and he took her hands in his. 'Please? I can't do anything on the barn with this hand like it is, and it gets pretty lonely and boring up there with just the dog for company. You could lock yourself in the car if you liked and talk to me through a crack in the top of the window, if you'd feel safer.'

'I might do that,' she said, but in the event it wasn't necessary. Shortly after she arrived her guardian angel provided chaperones in the guise of Ryan O'Connor and his two small children, and Jill was disturbed to feel a flicker of disappointment that she wouldn't have Zach to herself.

'Are we interrupting?' Ryan asked diplomatically.

Zach chuckled. 'No. In fact, this could be a good idea. Jill doesn't trust me to behave myself, so you can chaperone. You know Jill Craig, don't you?'

He nodded, reached over and grasped Jill's hand in his and shook it firmly, his firm, full mouth quirking with laughter at Zach's words. 'Happy to oblige. Jill, these are my children, Evie and Gus. Kids, say hello to Miss Craig.'

'Hello,' the children chorused.

'Uncle Zach, can we take Scud for a walk?' Evie asked, turning her pretty little face up to Zach.

He melted like a marshmallow in the sun. 'Sure, sweetheart, if your daddy says you can.'

Ryan nodded, his tawny hair gleaming gold in the sun— so much like Evie's. 'Don't go too far, Evie. Just around the back here. Don't go in the wood.'

'Oh, but I like the wood, Daddy!'

Her pout was pretty and should have melted Ryan's heart. Jill was impressed to see that it didn't. 'Just here, or not at all,' he repeated firmly.

Her little face quivered, but he was unmoved. 'OK, then,' she agreed. 'Shall we put him on the lead?'

'I think so.' Zach fetched the dog's lead, clipped it onto his collar and handed it to Evie. Instantly Scud settled down and walked sedately beside her instead of dancing excitedly at Zach's feet, and Ryan grinned.

'Poor dog. He thought he was getting a real walk.'

'I'll take him later,' Zach promised. 'Come and see the barn. It's progressed.'

Ryan nodded at his hand. 'How's the damage?'

'Healing. Still sore and a bit stiff.' He pulled a mournful face. 'It needs love, but Jill won't play.'

Ryan snorted. 'Wise girl. This guy's got a glibber tongue than I have, and I've got the Irish in me. No, Jill, you don't want to trust him. I'm a much safer bet.'

She laughed at them both. 'You're as bad as each other. A girl just isn't safe around either of you.'

Laughing, they went into the barn to examine the beam that had been the cause of Zach's injury, and Jill was horrified to see that it was up at head height. 'You could have been killed!' she exclaimed.

'She cares!' Zach said to Ryan, and grinned.

'Hmph. In your dreams.'

'Ah, now, if Ryan wasn't here I could tell you about my dreams. . .'

Ryan chuckled. 'Down, boy. I thought I was supposed to be chaperoning you two? Show me the plans of your drains or something mundane like that; take your mind off her.'

Jill smiled and left them to it, poring over plans and pointing at the rafters. Not quite the drains, but as good as. She put the kettle on, washed up some mugs and wandered out into the sunshine to see if the children were all right.

There was no sign of them, of course. She wandered round the side of the barn and spotted them in the field, just a few yards away from the barn, picking primroses along the bottom of the hedge. It was illegal, of course, to pick wild flowers, but there seemed to be hundreds of primroses and the children's faces were so intent that she didn't have the heart to stop them.

'Who are the flowers for?' she asked instead.

'Uncle Zach,' Gus said, 'cos he's got a sore hand.'

'We thought it might cheer him up.'

'Good idea.' Jill crouched down beside them and patted Scud, who was lying patiently in the grass waiting for the rest of his walk. 'So, tell me about yourselves. How old are you, Evie?'

'Five—nearly six, and Gus is four.'

'Nearly five.'

'Not till July. My birthday's in May. He's not at proper school yet, not till next term.' It was said with some satisfaction, and Jill stifled her smile.

'So, Gus, do you go to nursery school?'

He nodded. 'We do painting, and singing, and letters, and sometimes we go to the zoo.'

'Only once.'

Good grief, Jill thought, she certainly keeps her little brother in order! 'Did you enjoy it?'

He nodded again. 'Specially the tigers. They had very big teeth.'

His eyes were like saucers, and she found her mouth curving again in response. What lovely children, she thought, and how sad that they had lost their mother. Sad for her, to miss so much of such delightful children, and sad for them that they would never have a mother's love to comfort them.

She blinked away the sudden moisture in her eyes and stood up. 'I tell you what, shall we go in and give Uncle Zach the flowers before they go all floppy?'

They went in, Gus's hand trustingly in hers, Scud still firmly attached to Evie and trying hard not to drag her over. Evie held the flowers out to Zach. 'Here,' she said, 'because you're sore. They're to make you better—you'll have to put them in water or they'll hang down and go all brown.'

Zach crouched down and took the flowers from her, staring down at them for an endless moment. Jill could see his jaw working, as if Evie's gesture had moved him deeply, and she felt a sudden well of affection for him.

Or was it love? She took a deep breath as he tipped his head up and looked at Evie with very bright eyes. 'Thank you, sweetheart,' he said, and his voice was gravelly and a little choked. 'That's very kind.'

'They're from me too,' Gus added, and Zach turned to him.

'Are they? Well, thank you as well, then. I'll put them in water now.'

And he stood up and fished around for a small glass to put the mangled little primroses into, while Jill made three cups of coffee and offered the children a cold drink.

They took the drinks outside onto what was going to be the patio and Scud, released from his lead, set off across the field with his nose to a trail and just the waving plume of his tail visible above the tufts of grass.

'This is such a fantastic spot,' Ryan said, stretching his long legs out and giving a lazy sigh. 'I could sit here for ever and just listen to the birds.'

'It gets a bit much at five in the morning,' Zach said drily.

They laughed, and Ryan twisted round and peered back at the barn. 'So, when did you buy this heap?'

'Heap?' Zach said in mock indignation.

Ryan grinned. 'Just a figure of speech.'

Zach chuckled. 'Many a true word and all that. I saw it just a couple of months ago—after I knew I had the job.'

'Good choice. Ann always wanted something like this. She would have loved it.'

His face was empty of expression, with no obvious sign of sadness, and yet Jill sensed a great well of loneliness in the friendly man. It was a loneliness she'd sensed in Zach, too, and she wondered if that was what had drawn them together.

'How long have you two known each other?' she asked.

'Couple of weeks,' Ryan said with a shrug. 'We met on the squash court.'

Jill was surprised, and said so. 'I thought you'd known each other for ages.'

Zach gave a lopsided grin. 'Sometimes it feels like that. I suppose we've got a lot in common. Too much work and not enough play, for instance.'

Ryan chuckled ruefully. 'Sounds about like it. Oh, well,

life's pretty good, I guess. I've got two great kids and a job I love—it could be a whole hell of a lot worse.'

Jill supposed that it could, but it took a philosophical man to say so after losing his wife so tragically young. She must ask Zach how she had died.

The conversation ebbed and flowed around them, and then Ryan stood up and stretched. 'It's wonderful here, I could stay for ever,' he said with a sigh, and Jill had to agree. It was wonderful, and she would like nothing more than to share it with Zach for the rest of her life.

She might as well have wanted to fly, though, because there was no more chance of it happening. Unlike Ryan, he just wasn't the settling-down type—definitely not husband material!

Perhaps she should just throw caution to the winds and have a good fling. It might do her good after so long to relax and enjoy life—even if it would inevitably lead to her heart being smashed into a million pieces. . .

Zach didn't give her a chance to fling. Taking her at her word, he kept at a safe distance most of the time—moving closer only in snatched moments to tease and torment her miserable senses with a touch or a kiss or a flirting comment.

Only when it was safe did he allow himself to touch her. As she handed him notes, his fingers would close over hers for a second and squeeze. Once she held them cradled against her chest and he took them from her, the backs of his fingers brushing deliberately against her breast while his eyes danced with mischief.

Then Brian Birkett came onto the ward in defiance of the court order, and their careful plans fell apart.

Jill was passing the door of Mrs Birkett's room when she saw a movement. To her horror she realised that the woman's husband was there and had pulled a gun out of his coat pocket and was aiming it at his sleeping wife. Without thinking, she hurled herself at him and hit him squarely in the back, knocking him off balance.

There was a sharp pop and he wheeled away, flinging her to the ground. There was another pop and plaster dust sprayed off the wall beside her ear. Then he was gone, sprinting out of the ward before anyone could stop him.

Zach was at her side in seconds, his trembling hands running over her body and checking her for damage. 'Are you hurt? Did he get you?'

She shook her head, only dimly realising what had happened. 'No. No, he didn't. What about Dolly?'

Zach left her for a moment and checked the terrified woman, then ran for the door. 'Call Security,' he snapped. 'Get the police onto him pronto.'

Jill struggled to her feet and watched in horror as Zach headed after Birkett. Mary O'Brien was talking urgently down the phone, presumably to Security, and then one of the other nurses was there with her, steadying her as she brushed herself down and tried to stand straight on her trembling legs.

'Are you OK?' Mary asked, appearing in the doorway.

OK? Oh, sure, she thought with near hysteria. I've been shot at and nearly killed by a lunatic—all in a day's work! 'I'll live,' she muttered. 'How about Dolly?'

It all became very confused after that. A policeman came and interviewed her, asking the same questions over and over again, and Zach was hovering in the background looking thunderous. Apparently Birkett had slipped through the security net on the way out as well, and the police had lost him.

Finally satisfied with her statement, the police went and Zach took her home.

'I'll be fine,' she kept assuring him, but her legs felt as if they'd been left out in the rain and had gone soggy, and her eyes seemed to have developed a regrettable tendency to overflow.

He made her a cup of tea, laced with about half a packet of sugar, and forced her to drink the disgusting brew. Then he took the cup from her and pulled her onto his lap, and held her while she cried.

'He tried to kill me,' she said later when the tears had fizzled out and she could speak again.

Zach's arms tightened around her shoulders and she snuggled closer. 'Thanks for being here,' she mumbled into his neck.

'Don't thank me. I'm busy assuring myself you're still alive.'

She lifted her head and gave him a watery smile, then brushed her lips over his. 'I'm alive,' she whispered.

Then she lowered her head and settled her lips against his and one of his hands slid up and threaded through her hair, holding her steady as his mouth opened under hers and he deepened the kiss. She sighed into his mouth and let him turn her so that her weight was against the arm of the chair and his body was half turned across her, and she slid her arms up round his neck and drew his head down again for another kiss.

Time melted away. Their lips clung—their tongues mating and retreating, playing tag—humour and desire mingling as they toyed with each other. Then, finally, just when desire was beginning to get the upper hand, Zach lifted his head and touched her lips with his fingertips.

'Beautiful,' he murmured. 'So beautiful. Come home with me.'

'Why?'

'Because I want you, and you want me, and I have to get back for the dog.'

She lay there in his arms, staring up into his gorgeous midnight-blue eyes, and sighed. 'We weren't going to do this.'

'We don't have to,' he said, and she could tell that he meant it. 'I just don't feel ready to let you go yet.'

'If I come home with you we'll end up in bed together; you know we will.'

'Come for a while.'

She wanted to, but she couldn't. From somewhere within her she dredged up a last shred of common sense and shook her head. 'No. I'll be fine, Zach. You go home to the dog, and I'll have an early night.'

He sighed. 'I can't do that. The police don't want you left alone, not while Birkett's on the loose.'

She pulled away. 'So you're just here following orders?' she asked in a monotone.

He tugged her back into his arms. 'For God's sake, Jilly, don't be daft. There's no way I'd just let you go whatever the police had said, but I have to agree with them. I don't think you should be left alone, no matter what, so forget it. Either you come to my house for the night, or you come with me to fetch the dog and we all stay here. Take your pick.'

'I'm not allowed a dog here.'

'OK. You've got five minutes to pack.'

'I won't sleep with you,' she warned, wondering how she would stop him if he wouldn't listen to her.

'Fine. Just pack.'

He wasn't arguing enough, she thought absently as she hurled some things into a soft sports bag. He was obviously going to wait until they were at the barn before trying to talk her back into bed. Well, she wouldn't go. He could talk all he liked. She wanted distance, and she'd have it.

She got it—and some to spare. Zach, clearly deciding that he didn't trust himself, fed her and tucked her up in bed, told Scud to lie at her feet and went outside with a sleeping-bag.

'Where are you going?' she asked, puzzled.

'I'll sleep in the car,' he told her drily. 'You wanted to be able to trust me. I'm just making sure you can.'

And the door closed with an emphatic click.

Scud didn't waste a second. He was up on the bed, his huge head on the pillow beside her, grinning intelligently. If she hadn't known better she'd think he was trying to strike a deal with her.

'You're a monster, Scud, and you've got fish-breath. You'll have to face the other way.'

His tongue swiped over her face and he dropped his head onto his paws with a sigh. Jill turned her back on him, scrubbed her face on the quilt and fell instantly asleep.

She wouldn't have slept so well had she known that Zach was lying outside awake, his eyes straining on the track and watching for any sign of Birkett. There was no guarantee that he would connect Jill to this place, or that he would have found it, but Zach just felt a need for caution.

Besides, it gave him something to do to take his mind off the burning ache that was the legacy of his desire.

He wished that he smoked. They did in all the best cop movies. Oh, hell, he wanted her. She just felt so good in his arms. He'd tried so hard to keep out of her way and not touch her, but tonight he'd had no choice but to hold her and it had blown his resolve to smithereens.

Damn her and her soft grey eyes and warm, sleek body.

He groaned, shifting in his seat to ease the ache, and then he froze. Was that a movement down by the hedge?

Surely not. Probably a fox. It was all the hormones, curd-
ling his mind and making his imagination work overtime.

He settled back against the seat and closed his eyes,
and immediately saw her body stretched out on his bed—
a smile of welcome on her lips. Oh, hell. . .

Jill woke suddenly, unsure what had disturbed her. Scud's
head was lifted, his ears pricked. Zach, coming in for
something?

The lock scraped, and a low growl came from
Scud's thoat.

'Shut up, dog, it's Zach,' she mumbled sleepily.

Then without warning he leapt to his feet and barked
furiously, and she heard a familiar sharp pop and Scud
fell on her with an agonised yelp. There were more pops,
another yelp, and then the door slammed and she heard
pounding feet and Zach's voice raised in anger.

Oh, please, God, don't let him tackle him, she prayed,
and fumbling for the lamp she turned it on just as Zach
burst into the barn.

'He's gone. Are you all right? Jilly, speak to me!'

She looked up into his frantic eyes and reached out to
him. 'I'm fine. Zach, he hit Scud. . .'

He dropped to his knees beside the dog and reached
out, laying a hand on his heaving side. 'Scud? It's all
right, boy, I'm here. Jilly, ring the police and tell them
he's headed back to town, and then call the vet. The
number's by the phone. He's bleeding—damn.'

She heard a ripping noise and saw Zach wadding up
the remains of a pillowcase and pressing it against the
dog's neck. She called the police, then rang the vet and
all the time she could only think that if it hadn't been for
Scud that bullet would have hit her.

She put the receiver down, went behind the curtain and

threw up into the loo, then washed her face, dried it and went back.

'What can I do?' she asked calmly.

He met her eyes, his own wild with worry and fear. 'Start the car and back it up to the patio. We'll carry him out that way.'

She moved the car, opened the French doors and helped him shift the big, heavy dog onto a blanket. Then they loaded him into the back seat of Zach's car and he knelt in the cramped space behind the passenger seat, his hand still holding the pressure pad to the dog's neck, and directed her to the vet.

It was a nightmare drive at high speed over unfamiliar roads in a strange car, with Zach pleading with her to go faster and Scud's life ebbing away beneath his hands. Finally, though, they skidded into the car park at the vet's to find the lights on and a reception committee at the door.

Then suddenly there was nothing to do but wait, her fingers linked with Zach's bloodstained ones, while the vet fought to save Scud.

At last the door opened and the vet emerged, smiling reassuringly. 'He'll be OK. He's lost a lot of blood but there's no serious damage. He's on a drip and he'll be sedated for a while, but he should be back with you in a few days as good as new.'

Zach made a sound like a strangled sob and tipped his head back, his thoat working as he struggled to contain his emotion. Then he gave the vet a shaky grin. 'Thanks. He's—ah—my sister's dog. We're all very fond of him—' His voice cracked and Jill squeezed his hand tightly. He returned the pressure, and shot her a grateful smile. 'I suppose we should go to the police station now.'

She returned the smile. 'Probably. I imagine they'll be wondering where we both are.'

They were, but there was no great urgency now. The police had picked up Brian Birkett's car speeding down the lanes away from the barn, and in the ensuing chase he had misjudged a bend. As the detective explained to them, he wouldn't be a danger to his wife or to anyone else ever again.

There was one other problem, too. Someone, probably Birkett on the way to the barn, had smashed her bedroom window at the front of the house on the ground floor and fired several times into her bed.

'I shouldn't go back there tonight, if I were you,' the policeman advised. 'The landlord's been called and he's had the window boarded up, but the glass on the floor needs dealing with and Forensic are checking out the bullets just to be on the safe side. It seems pretty certain it's the same man, though. There aren't too many nutters like that around, thank God. Oh, and they've finished up at your barn, sir, and secured it, but I wouldn't go back there, either. Bit of a mess, what with the dog being shot and all that.'

Jill stared up at Zach in numb disbelief. 'Where can we go?' she said blankly.

'Ryan's. He'll put us up for the rest of the night.' He gave the policeman the address in case they needed to be contacted, and then led Jill out to his car. He pushed her into the seat and fastened her safety belt, then came round beside her and got behind the wheel. 'OK?' he murmured.

She nodded. 'I'll live.'

It was an unfortunate choice of words, and shocked them both. With a muttered curse Zach leant across and wrapped his arms around Jill. He was trembling, and she dropped her head against his shoulder and gave a tearful laugh. 'Sorry,' she mumbled. 'Shall I rephrase that?'

He straightened and dropped a kiss on her lips. 'Don't bother. Come on, let's get over to Ryan's.'

They turned into the drive of a pleasant detached house in the suburbs, and the outside security lights came on as they climbed out of the car and flooded the front of the house with welcoming light. Jill was glad. She didn't think she could bear to be in the dark ever again. Zach leant on the bell for a few seconds, the lights in the house flicked on one by one and they could hear footsteps on the stairs.

She leant against Zach as she waited for the door to open and then Ryan was there, his face shocked as he took in their dishevelled appearance and Zach's brief account of the past few hours.

'My God—come in, for heaven's sake.' He ushered them into the living-room and shook his head in disbelief. 'Heck, you look all washed up. Let me fix you a drink. Scotch? Brandy?'

'Tea?' Jill said wearily. 'I could just murder a cup of tea—oh, Zach—'

She turned into Zach's waiting arms, her choice of words again bringing back the full horror of the evening. He dragged her hard up against his chest, wrapped his arms round her like steel bands and hugged her so hard that she thought her ribs would break.

It felt wonderful.

She didn't cry. She was too shocked, too scared, too everything to let go. Instead she just stood there, hugging him back, and let him rock her gently in his arms until the tension went out of them both a little and she could start to breathe again.

Then Ryan shoved a brandy into one of her hands and a cup of tea into the other, did the same to Zach and pushed them gently down onto the settee.

'Would you like to run this by me again?' he asked.

So Zach did, starting at the beginning with Dolly Birkett's admission, and gradually it began to make sense to Jill.

'He was targeting me because I overheard that conversation, wasn't he?' she murmured.

'I would imagine so,' Zach said gently. 'Anyway, it's all over now, sweetheart. He won't go after you again.'

'Or you.' She looked up at his beloved face, and imagined it cold and lifeless. As hers would have been had it not been for the dog. 'Phone the vet,' she urged.

So he did, and came back with the news that Scud was doing fine. 'He'll call here if there's any change.'

Ryan nodded. 'Fine. Hopefully you'll hear nothing. Now, about rooms. One or two?'

'One,' they said together, and Zach gave a quiet snort. 'Yes, one. I'm not letting her out of my sight again.'

'How about if I give you the twin room?'

Zach's grin was wry. 'Fine.'

They slept in one bed, though, locked tightly in each other's arms. There was no question of making love. They were both too shocked and tired to even think of it.

Until the morning.

Then Zach woke her with a tender kiss that turned into a raging inferno in seconds, and only Ryan's quiet knock at the door dragged them back from the edge of insanity.

He opened the door a chink and spoke through the gap. 'I've called the hospital and told them you won't be in. I'm just taking the kids to the child-minder and then I'm off to work. Make yourselves at home.' The door clicked quietly shut, they heard muted voices downstairs and then all was quiet.

Zach threw back the covers and stood up, going over to the window and staring out at the brand new day.

'She'll be safe now,' he said softly.

'Dolly?'

'Mmm. I'm going to call the vet. Want a cup of tea?'

'I'd love one.'

'Stay there.'

He went out and left her lying in the bed, listening to the sound of the morning traffic and the birds singing in the trees outside, and it all seemed so sunny and normal and safe that she closed her eyes and snuggled down on the pillow again and slid quietly into oblivion.

Zach, coming back in with her tea a few minutes later, found her fast asleep, one hand flung up like a child's and her lashes dark crescents against her pale cheeks. Dear God, she looked so vulnerable, so frail, so incredibly dear.

It was a good job that Birkett was dead.

CHAPTER FIVE

JILL woke at eleven, with the sun streaming in through the window and Zach stretched out on the other bed watching her.

'OK?' he asked softly.

'Mmm. What are you doing?'

'Lying here watching you sleep.'

'How boring.'

'Not at all.'

Their eyes locked and Jill felt her heart shift and shiver. She smiled, a soft, sleepy smile, warm and inviting, and Zach got off the other bed and lay down beside her, pulling her into his arms.

'You look beautiful in the morning,' he murmured against her ear.

She knew he was lying, but it sounded so good that she didn't bother to challenge him. Anyway, the look in his eyes made her feel beautiful. If only she could believe it, but she'd seen him look at the old dears like that. She snuggled her face into his rough, bristly neck and sighed in contentment. So what if he was nice to them too? He was with her for now, and she was going to enjoy it.

'We ought to go and see Dolly,' he said quietly after a while.

'Mmm. I don't know what to say to her.'

He hugged her gently. 'You'll think of something. I imagine she'll want to thank you for saving her life before you get a word in edgeways, anyway. I don't know what you were thinking about running in there like that and tackling him barehanded.'

'He had a gun. He was going to shoot her!'

'I noticed,' he said drily. 'He also tried to shoot you—three times, in fact.'

'Twice. The third time he was expecting it to be you, but why he should want to kill you I don't know.'

'Unless he realised you weren't at your flat after all.'

She shuddered. 'Whatever. He's dead and we're all OK, even poor old Scud. Did the vet say what had happened?'

'Nicked the jugular vein. He was lucky it wasn't deeper, or the carotid artery. The other bullet went through his back leg but doesn't seem to have done a great deal of harm. He'll limp a bit for a while.'

'Poor old Scud. If he hadn't been there—'

Zach's arms tightened convulsively. 'Don't. I'll never tell him off for sleeping on the bed again, I swear.'

'He'll be spoilt.'

'He is already. What's new?'

They chuckled, and then Zach eased away a little and peered down at her. 'Fancy a shower while I make your breakfast?'

'I could do with some clean clothes.'

'We'll go and have a look at both places in a while. Just get yourself cleaned up and we'll go from there.'

He swung his legs to the floor and stood up and, without thinking, Jill threw back the bedclothes and got out of bed.

Zach's eyes fastened hungrily on her body, clad only in a bra and pants, and she flushed a little and froze while the air sizzled between them. He was just three strides away. It would be so easy to reach him—

Then he mumbled, 'I'll get your breakfast,' and shot out of the door. She sagged back onto the bed and sat there wondering why on earth she was bothering to keep him at a distance.

She wanted him; he wanted her—so what if he was a flirt? So what if she couldn't trust him long-term? Heavens, it wasn't as if sleeping together was going to break any new ground—they'd already done it once.

And how.

Her skin heated at the memory, and it was all she could do not to go downstairs and jump on him in the kitchen.

No. She'd wait until they were back in their own territory, his or hers—preferably his, although there would be some ghosts to lay there before she could sleep in that bed again.

And what better way to lay them?

She smiled, a soft, womanly smile, and hummed quietly as she headed down the hall looking for the bathroom. There was a damp towel on the edge of the bath, which looked as if Zach had used it. She showered swiftly, pulled her dirty clothes back on and ran downstairs.

'What should we do with the beds?'

'Leave them. We may be back tonight.'

'OK.' She sat down at the table, obediently ate the toast and marmalade he pushed under her nose, and drank two cups of tea straight down. 'Wow, that's better. Right, now for Dolly.'

'As you say.'

Things gradually got back to normal over the next few days. Jill's flat was cleaned up and the window repaired, and her landlord bought her a new bed. Zach decorated the room and together they went out and bought new bed linen for both beds to replace the items damaged in the shootings.

Scud made excellent progress, and Jill was extremely

relieved to see him looking well again. She was convinced that if it hadn't been for the dog she might well have died, and she resolved never to resent his enthusiastic greetings or bad breath ever again.

As for Dolly Birkett, she was very subdued and shaken, but in a strange way Jill sensed a lightening of her spirits—as if a huge fear had gone away and she was now at peace. She said nothing, though, apart from thanking Jill for saving her life and apologising for all the trouble she'd caused. Jill found that she was unable to talk to her about it in any depth. Her own feelings were much too deeply involved, and she was very conscious that the bullet that had hit Scud had, in fact, been meant for Zach.

It was only after several days had passed that Dolly Birkett actually spoke to Jill about her husband, and Jill realised that it was, in fact, the day of his funeral.

'I still loved him, in a way,' she said sadly. 'Silly, isn't it, after all he did to everyone but, you know, he wasn't all bad. When we first married he was a good man. It was losing his job that finished him—that and drink, though it's hard to say which came first.'

Jill suspected that drink might have been the cause of him losing his job, but it wasn't her place to say so. Instead she let Dolly talk, and gradually all the fears and hatred and terrible injustices came out—the beatings and insults, the degradation, the criticism—all the signs of a damaged ego run mad.

And yet she had loved him. Jill found that quite amazing, but while nursing the woman she'd realised that she had depths of courage that few people ever dreamed of tapping into. Her legs were gradually healing, but her right foot was slow to mend and Robert Ryder was unhappy about it.

'If it doesn't show signs of progress soon he wants to

put an electrical stimulator in to try and trigger healing,'
Zach told Jill, a few days after the funeral.

'But we can't do that here,' she said.

'No. She'd have to be transferred to a specialist centre.'

'Oh.'

'Oh?'

Jill smiled. 'I'll miss her. She's in constant pain and
yet she's got so much guts.'

Zach gave her a quizzical look. 'I would have thought
you'd be glad to see her go. She must remind you daily
of what happened.'

'No. Well, yes, but what she reminds me of more is
our amazing resilience. She lived for years with the threat
of his unpredictable violence, and she's still sane. I find
that quite remarkable. One night was enough for me.'

'Me too.' Zach shot her a tentative smile. 'Are you
really all right now? No nightmares?'

'No, no nightmares. How about you?'

His smile was wry. 'I could do with some company at
night, but it's not a lot to do with nightmares and more
to do with missing you. That one night with you in my
arms at Ryan's was enough to give me a taste for it.'

Jill looked away. His eyes were smouldering, and heat
licked along her veins. She, too, had found the nights
lonely and empty without him. How could you get so used
to something in such a short time that it left such an aching
void when it was gone?

One night, that was all, and that a night without passion.
But she still felt strange about the barn, and she supposed
she always would. Brian Birkett's attack had scarred her
more deeply than she'd realised.

'How about dinner?' Zach asked quietly.

Her eyes flew back to his. 'Dinner?' she repeated.

'Tonight. I'll take you out. It's Friday. We could stay out late and not worry.'

He made it sound like a date. Not like their other meals and walks and evenings spent tackling the barn, but dinner. Something special, different.

Like he was courting her.

Grief, what an old-fashioned concept to attach to someone like Zach, but that was how it felt.

'Dinner?' she said again.

'Not if you don't want to. We could go for a walk or paint a wall or watch television at your flat—whatever.'

Oh. So he didn't mean it to sound special. Jill, ready to refuse his invitation, now perversely found herself disappointed. Their relationship had reached a sort of stalemate since the shootings, and she didn't know whether to be glad or sorry that he didn't mean to change things.

'Let's do something to the barn,' she suggested.

Did he look disappointed? Surely not! She was going nuts.

'Fine,' he agreed easily. 'Do you want to go home and change and I'll see you there in a little while?'

'OK.'

So she went home and pulled on old clothes, then went with Zach to the barn where they heaved plasterboard about and created stud walls downstairs. At midnight they stood back and examined their handiwork, and Zach grinned tiredly. 'Progress,' he said.

'Mmm.' Jill thought it was a lot better because suddenly the barn wasn't just a yawning void, and it was no longer possible to sit on the bed and see the door where Brian Birkett had stood to shoot at her.

As for Scud, he was back to his normal boisterous self and seemed totally unaffected by the changes. His only problem was dashing through the kitchen and heading for the bed, then crashing into a wall which had appeared on the far side of the kitchen table.

'Poor boy,' Zach crooned lovingly, rubbing his head and soothing his damaged pride. 'You'll have to look where you're going, son.'

Jill laughed, and the laugh turned into a yawn.

Zach immediately looked at his watch and swore softly. 'I'll take you home. I had no idea it was so late.'

I could stay, she wanted to say, but she couldn't seem to make her tongue form the words, and so she said goodbye to Scud and let Zach drive her back to her lonely flat.

'Coming in for coffee?' she offered hopefully.

He hesitated, then shook his head. 'Better not,' he said enigmatically, and Jill was left alone with just a brief kiss—to wonder if he now regretted their precipitate intimacy and the dramatic events that had followed.

Perhaps, as he had said so many weeks ago now, he just wanted a companion?

That being the case, she thought, it was a shame she had allowed herself to fall so deeply in love with him. . .

Zach drove home alone for the zillionth time and fell into bed to lie staring sleeplessly at the ceiling and wondering if he dared to push Jill again to move their relationship forward. She had taken such an emotional battering that he was reluctant to make a move in case she came to him for comfort rather than for the right reasons.

He was still unsure how much Gordon had to do with their first sexual encounter. He wanted the next one to be because she wanted to be with him, and not because she wanted to banish images that haunted her.

Above all, he dreaded looking into her eyes and seeing regret.

So he resolved yet again to do nothing, and glared at

the ceiling until it was a miracle that it didn't catch fire
or melt. . .

Jill only had a short weekend off. She was back in the
ward on Sunday morning, and weighing the cost of the
previous night's foolishness in the town.

There was a drunk with a broken jaw waiting for the
maxillary-facial surgeon to stick him back together again,
a couple who had been cut free from their car after it had
been in collision with a pair of youngsters joyriding, and
the joyriders themselves—or at least one of them. The
other, a young female passenger, was in intensive care
and would probably stay there at least until the following
morning.

Steve Smith, the driver of the stolen car, was sixteen,
scared to death and suffering from two broken legs and a
broken arm. Jill, meeting his parents later, thought it likely
that his father would break the other arm if left alone with
him for long.

They were furious, tremendously disappointed in their
son and extremely worried about the young girl in ITU,
Helen Lawford—the daughter of a neighbour and friend.

They didn't stay long—just long enough to make sure
that he would be all right and express their grave disappointment, and then they left.

Mary and Jill decided to put Steve Smith next to Jason
Bridger, the young motorcyclist who had wrapped his bike
round a tree and given his pillion passenger head injuries—fortunately fleeting. Jason's injuries were much
slower to heal, of course, with his two fractured femurs,
and he was still on traction and as grumpy as one might
expect after six weeks. He still had several weeks to go
before he could be allowed up and about, and the ward staff
were wondering how they could cope with his boredom.

'Perhaps he'll get on well with Steve Smith and they'll entertain each other,' Jill said optimistically.

Mary laughed. 'More likely egg each other on. I'm not sure what's worse—Jason grumpy or Jason full of high spirits!'

However, Jason's high spirits were doomed to failure. The routine X-ray to ensure that his traction was being effective proved that the left femur was failing to maintain alignment, and Robert Ryder felt that it would be better after all to pin it to encourage speedier healing. The other leg was doing well and showing signs of forming a healthy callus across the break, and if the left one was pinned the boy would be up and about much sooner.

Zach operated on him on the Tuesday, and by Friday he was feeling much more perky. So was Steve Smith, and the pair of them were promptly dubbed the Terrible Twins.

Helen Lawford, on the other hand, was also transferred to the ward after a few days and she was in a much more serious condition. She was put in the room Dolly had been in, and Dolly was out on the main ward and quietly enjoying the company of the other women. Helen, though, was not in any state to enjoy anything and Jill wondered if Steve was actually aware of how ill she was. She decided that he couldn't possibly be, and wasn't sure if that was a good thing or not.

Zach, though, was well aware of her condition and he was worried about her.

'I don't know if she's going to make it,' he said quietly as they walked away from her little room on the Friday afternoon.

'Anything in particular?'

He shrugged. 'Just a gut feeling. She's been scanned, X-rayed, checked over to within an inch of her life, but I still get the feeling she's worse than we realise. I just feel we're sitting on a time bomb.'

Jill, too, had felt the same about patients before and she wasn't usually wrong. For that reason she trusted Zach's instinct and put another nurse on to special Helen over the weekend, even though she was technically now stable enough not to need so much attention.

Zach crawled over the X-rays and scans again with a fine tooth comb, certain that they were missing something obvious, but there was nothing.

Finally he gave up. 'I can't see it. Whatever it is, I can't find it. Perhaps I'm wrong. Perhaps her progress is just slow.'

Like ours, Jill thought. 'How's the barn coming on?' she asked, angling for an invitation.

He laughed softly. 'Not fast. Fancy spending a few hours heaving chipboard about? I want to lay the floor upstairs. I've got the stairs in and the oak boards down on the landing area, but I need help with the other stuff.'

'Sure.'

'Then I can get the bed upstairs and I'll feel I'm making progress.'

And Brian Birkett's ghost would be well and truly laid. 'When shall we start?' Jill asked with a grin.

'Now?'

She nodded. 'I'll nip across the back way and grab a few things, and meet you at my flat in fifteen minutes. All right?'

'Ten.'

'Whatever. You can wait if I'm not ready.'

She almost ran home, grabbing clothes from her bedroom and shoving them into a bag then hesitating for a moment before opening the drawer of her dressing-table and lifting out a little packet.

She chewed her lip and studied it. She'd never bought condoms before. She'd nearly died of embarrassment buying these in the supermarket. Heaven knows if they were the right sort. Did they come in different sizes, like shoes? No. Despite her ignorance, she knew that there was sufficient elasticity in them to cater for any but the most extreme variations.

She didn't think Zach qualified as that extreme. Either that or she was, too, because they'd seemed a remarkably good match—

The bell dragged her out of her quandary. She shoved the packet into her bag, zipped the top and ran for the door.

'I'm ready,' she said breathlessly.

He grinned. 'So I see.' His finger flicked out and slid inside the neck of her shirt. 'You're buttoned up all wrong,' he murmured, and pushed her back into the hall, kicking the door shut gently.

'Oh.' Cheeks burning, she stood motionless as he unfastened her blouse and rearranged it, then bent to kiss her lightly on the lips.

'What's this?' he asked, taking her bag.

'Um—just a few things to change into in case I get dirty.'

That seemed to satisfy him. It was a good job he couldn't see inside, she thought, what with the condoms and her overnight things! Not to mention that lace contraption she'd bought some time ago and had never had the courage to wear. . .

'There!' Zach brushed off his hands, straightened up and grinned at Jill. '*Voila*! The floor. Now to get the bed up here.'

He ran past her and down the open stairway and she followed him more slowly, cautious of the lack of banisters. They would be coming, he assured her, but until then she was going to take it very steady!

He was ripping the sheets off the bed when she got downstairs, piling them in the corner and grabbing the handles on the side of the mattress. She took one of the handles and followed him up the stairs, with the mattress trailing and bumping along the outside edge, and finally they had it in the area which was destined to be Zach's bedroom.

The base followed, heavier but more co-operative, and then he chucked the mattress onto the base, threw himself backwards onto it and patted the space beside him. 'Come and admire the view,' he said.

She grinned. 'I am.'

He preened for her and she laughed and threw a pillow at him, then turned and ran back down the stairs as he jackknifed off the edge of the bed and lunged for her. He chased her round the barn then out through the doors and round the outside, with Scud barking furiously and joining in.

She headed for the back door but Zach was too quick for her and caught her just as she slipped through the door, tugging her back into his arms.

Then he kissed her, a sizzling, heart-stopping kiss that should have gone on for ever but for some reason didn't. He let her go without a word, stepping back and turning away, and then with a ragged sigh he rammed his hands through his hair and turned back to face her.

'We need to talk, Jilly,' he said with quiet emphasis. 'Let's get a drink and sit outside.'

Why so serious so suddenly? she wondered as she followed him inside. Was he going to end it? Please, God, no, not when she'd just plucked up the courage to move on in their relationship.

He picked up a bottle of wine from the kitchen table, found two glasses and headed out through the French doors to the patio. He poured their drinks and handed her one, then sat on one of the plastic chairs and stared out into the velvet night.

She sat near him on another chair, sipping her wine in silence and waiting for him to start, her heart in her mouth.

It took him an age. Finally he started speaking, his voice gravelly in the quiet night. 'I can't go on like this, Jilly,' he began. 'I promised I'd give you space, but I can't do it any more. I don't know what you want from me. I'm confused. I just know I can't carry on playing games like we have been and pretending I don't want you.'

'Do you want me?' she asked, her heart almost motionless with suspense.

He swivelled towards her, his face taut in the soft spill of light from the house. 'Dear God, Jill, don't you know?'

She looked down at her hands. Her heart was pounding now, her blood roaring in her ears. She could have laughed with relief if she hadn't been so close to tears. 'Could you bring me a jumper, please? It's in my bag.'

With a muttered curse he got to his feet and went inside. He was gone for ages, then finally he appeared in the doorway with the little packet in one hand and the lacy contraption in the other.

'Jilly?' he said in a strangled voice.

She stood up. 'I thought it was time we moved on,' she said, taking her courage in both hands.

His eyes slid shut for a long moment, then he opened them and in the darkness they seemed coal-black and burning with a quiet intensity. He waved the scrap of lace. 'Go and shower while I make up the bed. Then I'll shower while you pretty yourself up and put this on,' he said hoarsely and, turning on his heel, he ran up the stairs.

She went behind the curtain, stripped off the dusty jeans and shirt that she had worn for laying the floor and then stood under the shower for an age, praying for courage and hoping against hope that this wouldn't turn into a ghastly mistake.

Then, before he got sick of waiting and came and got her, she turned off the water, dried herself and ran upstairs swathed in the towel.

'It's all yours,' she told him as she passed him at the kitchen doorway.

'I need the towel,' he called after her.

She peeled it off and dropped it on him at the foot of the stairs, then went into what would be the bedroom. The bed was neatly made, the new white linen crisp and fresh, and lying on the top next to the packet of condoms was the little lace thing she had bought in a moment of madness.

She studied it for a moment, then pulled it over her head and fastened the little pearly studs at the bottom. Lord, how she wished she had a mirror. She chewed her lip and hovered, and a moment later decided to take it off.

She was a moment too late, though, because Zach reappeared, naked except for the towel in his hand, and his approval was immediate and obvious. She blushed and dragged her eyes up to his.

'I feel silly in it,' she muttered.

'Don't. You look spectacular.' He dropped the towel and moved towards her, his eyes burning holes in the lace.

At least, she felt as if they should have done. He reached out a hand and touched her nipples with his outspread fingers, chafing them both at once so they peaked and strained towards him.

'Zach—!'

Her breath caught and he bent his head and flicked his tongue over one nipple, curving his hard, warm hand around the other breast and cupping it lovingly. His other hand slid behind her and eased her towards him, and she felt the satin-and-steel nudge of his erection against her thigh.

Her legs nearly gave way, and she sagged against him with a tiny cry. He muttered something then lifted her in his arms, laid her gently on the bed and he knelt up and looked down at her.

'You're beautiful,' he murmured. 'So beautiful.'

His hand moved to the leg of the lace confection, one finger gliding under the elastic and sliding round—brushing over the soft, dewy mound so scarcely concealed by the gauzy fabric.

'Zach, please!' she breathed.

'Please what? Please stop? Please more? Please something else?'

'Please—touch me.'

His eyes locked with hers for a moment, then he turned his hand and cupped her with its warmth. 'Does this thing have buttons?' he asked gruffly.

'Yes—well, studs.'

'Here?'

He dragged his eyes down and searched the fabric, then flicked the studs open with his hand and moved the lace away. She should have been embarrassed. For the life of her she couldn't understand why she wasn't, but when he bent his head and brushed a kiss against the dewy nest she all but wept with relief.

Her fingers threaded through his hair, soft and thick and so, so silky, and held him there while his tongue did magical things to her. Then suddenly, without warning, the world tilted on its axis and she fell headlong into a shuddering climax that left her breathless and confused.

As her heart steadied she found him beside her, his hand

resting over her quivering ribcage and his eyes locked on her face.

'All right?' he murmured.

She couldn't speak. The embarrassment she hadn't felt before tormented her now, and she turned her face into his shoulder with a little sob.

'Shh,' he murmured, and pulled her gently into his arms. 'Don't cry. Please don't cry.'

'I just feel so brazen,' she mumbled into his skin.

He laughed, a softly teasing laugh that didn't hurt, and kissed her shoulder, then her throat and then her lips. They parted for him and he slanted his mouth over hers and kissed her as if he were dying for her. Then after an age he lifted his head and stared into her eyes.

'OK now?'

She nodded, still shaken to her depths. 'I didn't know it could be so—no one ever said—I haven't—oh, God, Zach. . .'

'I've never done it before either,' he confessed. 'I've never wanted to, but with you it just seemed so right.'

'Never?' she whispered, incredulously.

'Never.'

She touched his cheek with her palm, loving the rough-smooth texture of his skin, the hard jut of his jaw, the burning fervour of his eyes. Her hand slid down his back, relishing the satin texture of his skin over the smooth, rippling muscles.

He shifted so that her hand could continue its journey round over his hip and down, until at last her palm was filled with the soft steel of his manhood. He groaned and dropped his head against her shoulder as her fingers curved round him and cupped the glorious fullness.

She explored him with her fingers, bold now after his confession, and then moved so that she could study him more closely with her eyes. Her lips trailed over the rigid plane of his abdomen, pressing hot, open-mouthed kisses over his clean, fresh skin. Lord, he was glorious—

'Jilly?'

'Mmm?' she murmured, distracted by the awe-inspiring beauty of his maleness.

'Please?'

She hesitated for a long moment, then bent her head and touched her tongue hesitantly to the dewy tip.

He bucked beneath her hand, his breath hissing out, and made bold by his response she followed her instincts. His fingers threaded through her hair, holding her still, and then suddenly he shuddered and drew her up against his chest.

'Stop,' he said raggedly. 'Give me a moment.' His heart was pounding, thundering against her ear, and she lay still against him and waited for his heart to steady. Then she lifted her head.

'I want you,' she told him. 'Now.'

'Condom,' he said succinctly.

Her eyes widened. 'I don't know where they are.'

'They must be here somewhere.'

She searched the bed furiously, but the packet remained elusive.

'I don't know where they've gone,' she said, her voice sharp with frustration. 'Zach, you must have some more.'

'I haven't. I didn't dare. It was the only thing that kept me away from you.'

'Oh.' She sat back on her heels. 'We can't, then. Not until we find them.'

'I need to be inside you,' he groaned. 'Now, Jilly. Not tomorrow, not the day after. Where the hell have they gone?'

He catapulted off the bed and stripped it, coming up victorious with the little packet in his hand.

She nearly collapsed with relief, and the relief made her laugh. Zach sat back down on the dishevelled bed and chuckled and then they were in each other's arms, laughing crazily at themselves until the laughter was pushed aside by their ever-present need.

Then Zach handed her a little foil wrapper. 'Here. You do the honours.'

'But I don't know how.'

'You didn't know about all sorts of things a little while ago, and you seem to be doing fine.'

'Oh.' She blushed, but with shaking fingers she completed her task. 'What now?'

He lay there against the pillows, a lazy smile on his mouth. 'Do you fancy driving?'

'Oh!'

'"Oh!"' yourself. Go on—and don't tell me you don't know how.'

'But I don't!'

'So learn. You're a quick study.'

She swallowed and moved over him, kneeling astride his hips then guiding him carefully she lowered herself.

Her eyes flew open. 'Oh! Zach!'

His eyes closed briefly, and when they opened they were ablaze again. 'Now move, just slowly—that's it—yesss!' His breath hissed out and he gripped her hips, guiding her into his rhythm.

She teased him, though—holding back, moving slowly, hovering—until he lost his patience and flipped her over. Then he rode her hard and fast, fine beads of sweat breaking out on his skin before he threw back his head and let out a great cry of release.

She felt the deep pulsing of his release just seconds

before her own, and then his hand was there, touching her, driving her even higher before she toppled over into oblivion. . .

CHAPTER SIX

THAT night marked the start of a blissful and glorious weekend. Zach and Jill worked on the barn during the day, and in the evening they settled down in the sunshine on the patio and relaxed. Then, when it grew too cool to sit outside any longer, they went up to Zach's bed and made love until a thin grey line appeared on the horizon.

Then they slept, wrapped in each other's arms, with Scud beside them banished to a rug on the floor snoring his disapproval.

By morning Scud was sprawled across the foot of the bed and they were curled up at the top like spoons, nestled into each other as if they'd been together for years.

They woke slowly, with languid kisses and gentle affection, and then made love in the shower before tackling breakfast and another day of work on the barn.

That evening, though, their peace was shattered by the ringing of the phone. It was the houseman on duty in the ward, concerned about Helen Lawford. Jill only got one side of the conversation, but it seemed that she had deteriorated and the houseman wasn't happy.

'Of course I don't mind,' Zach assured his junior colleague for the third time. 'I'll come right in.' He hung up and turned to Jill, a rueful expression on his face. 'Sorry, sweetheart. I'd better run you back—I don't know how long I'll be.'

'Want me to come in too?'

He shrugged. 'You could. I'll drop you at home to change if you like, or I could pop in and report to you.'

'I'll come in,' she decided. 'I'd like to see how she is for myself.'

The answer wasn't good. By the time Jill arrived Zach had ordered a chest X-ray and bloods, and was preparing to take an arterial blood sample for analysis of blood gases. Jill could see instantly that the girl had gone radically downhill since Friday. Her breathing was rapid and shallow, a typical response to a pulmonary problem, and Zach was afraid that she had developed a chest infection or alternatively an embolus of some sort.

'You don't think she's got fat embolism syndrome, do you?' Jill asked worriedly.

Zach chewed his lip, then nodded. 'Yes, I'm afraid she might have. With all the fractures she's sustained, it's quite possible there's fat circulating in her system. If it's broken down into tiny globules and lodged in her lungs, we may lose her.'

'Are you going to try steroids?'

'Yes—I think we might do that even before we get the results, just to be on the safe side. I've put her on oxygen, but all her other symptoms add up. She's drowsy; she's got petechial rashes here and there, her breathing's altered—I'm checking for platelets and serum lipase, but I expect them to be abnormal. We're checking her urine for fat now.'

Just then a student nurse came out of the sluice.

'Anything?' Zach asked.

'Maybe. I think there's something in her urine. Can you come and see?'

They went into the sluice and, sure enough, there was what looked like a fine, greasy film over the top of the urine sample.

'Get that down to the lab,' Zach said tiredly. 'Oh, and

better phone her parents and warn them that she's not too good and ask them to come in and sit with her.'

'They only just went home an hour or so ago.'

'Well, I think they'd better come back, regardless,' Zach said.

'Won't it worry them?' the girl persisted.

Zach sighed. 'Not as much as missing her death will. Just call them, please. Actually, on second thoughts, Jill, could you do it?'

'Of course.'

The student followed her into the office, her face shocked. 'Is she going to die?'

'We hope not, but if Zach's right it's possible.'

She dialled the number and told the mother, who answered the phone, that they were a little concerned about Helen's chest and she might appreciate some company as they had to run tests and so forth. Would they be able to come straight back?

'Why didn't you just tell them she was very ill?' the student asked.

'And worry them, possibly unnecessarily? Maybe even cause them to have an accident on the way? No. There's plenty of time to worry them after it's certain that's what she's got. It might just be a chest infection. Did you call X-Ray?'

She nodded. 'They said they were busy but would send someone up as soon as they could.'

Jill sighed and punched in a number. 'X-Ray? Hello, it's Sister Craig here on Orthopaedics One. We requested a portable X-ray up here on a patient some time ago. Would you send someone now, please? It's extremely urgent. No, it can't wait. Query fat embolism syndrome for chest screen, now, please. Thank you.'

She hung up. 'Why does this sort of thing always happen

at the weekend when there's no one about? Could you be a love and take the urine sample down to the lab, and tell them it's urgent? In capitals.'

The girl gave a weak smile. 'Sure. Sorry.'

Jill went back into the ward and found Zach preparing to take the blood gas sample. 'Hold her arm steady, could you? She's a bit past reasoning with.'

Jill sat on the bed, clamped the arm firmly across her lap and held it steady as Zach dug about in her wrist looking for the artery. He got it on the second try, and filled the syringe with the bright, oxygenated blood. 'Right, we want that down to Haematology fast, together with the other ones for platelets and serum lipase.'

'I'll take them. At least I'll make sure they know it's urgent.'

She took the bottles from his hands, shoved them in her pockets and grabbing the forms set off down the corridor at a swift walk. The lab technician rolled his eyes at her. 'Another urgent one, I suppose,' he said with a grin.

'You guessed. Can you call the results through?'

He nodded, and she headed back to the ward to find the girl's parents had arrived and were shocked to see the change in her.

'She looks grey,' her mother said, biting her lip. 'Whatever's wrong?'

'We don't know,' Zach said carefully. 'We're just waiting for some results so we can narrow the possibilities down a bit.'

'How long will that take?'

'Hopefully not too long. We're just waiting for the X-ray result at the moment. The blood tests will take a little while longer.'

Mrs Lawford pulled a chair up to her daughter's side, took her hand and started talking to her straight away. Mr

Lawford hovered uncertainly before drawing up another chair and sitting beside his wife, a comforting hand on her shoulder.

Jill could hardly bear to watch them. The diagnosis was almost certain, the prognosis awful. She organised the student to make the parents a cup of tea and went into the sister's office with Zach.

'Where the hell is that X-ray?' he muttered, just as the door opened and a porter came in.

'Films on Helen Lawford—they for you?'

Zach almost snatched the envelope out of his hand and tugging out the plates he snapped them up onto the screen, then swore softly.

Her lungs were both almost completely covered by grey spotty areas of patchy consolidation. Two lobes were completely obstructed, and the rest were on the way. Before Jill's eyes Zach seemed to crumple inside for a moment before he drew a deep breath and turned to her.

'She'd better go down to ITU.'

'I've already rung them. They haven't got a bed. The chest consultant is coming in.'

Zach swore again. 'She needs specialist care.'

'Then we'll have to give it to her, won't we?'

The consultant arrived with the blood results, confirmed Zach's diagnosis and went to tell Helen's parents the unhappy news. They were moved out to the day-room while he examined her, ordered intratracheal and systemic steroids and muttered under his breath.

'What's caused it?' Helen's mother had asked, but there was no satisfactory answer. It was just an unfortunate and very rare complication of fracture and, although there were theories, there was no conclusive evidence that would lead to any preventative measures.

And, unfortunately, there was no cure. It either got better or it didn't, depending on the severity of the case.

Helen's case was severe.

They worked on her all night, trying to improve her ventilation, but her lungs were filling with tiny little globules of fat and she was being literally suffocated before their eyes.

Shortly before three a.m. she lapsed into a coma, and at four-thirty she slid quietly away, with her parents standing at her side holding her hands and Jill, Zach and the consultant all visibly moved.

It was almost six before they went back to the barn and Jill, who desperately needed to cry her eyes out, found that Zach was silent and unapproachable and remote.

She made them breakfast without speaking, and handed him a plate. He stared at it for a long moment then, picking it up, he hurled it straight through the glass of the French doors.

'She was fifteen,' he said into the silence that followed. 'Fifteen, Jilly. That's no time to die—'

His voice cracked and he clamped his jaw hard, the muscles jumping as he struggled with his tumbling emotions.

'Why?' he whispered in anguish, and Jill, unable to stand back any longer, wrapped him in her arms and held him.

For an age he was stiff and unyielding, then finally he gave in and let go and they wept together for the tragic waste of Helen's life.

Then they kissed away the tears, made more breakfast and carried on—because they had to; because the world was still out there waiting and there were others who needed them.

That was medicine for you. No time to grieve, no time

to wallow in the injustice of it all; just pick yourself up and carry on.

Steve Smith, the driver of the car Helen had been in, was devastated. Apart from the shock and grief of the death of a close friend, he had to deal with his guilt because he had talked her into going in the car with him.

'She didn't want to come,' he wept. 'I made her come and now she's dead! I didn't want her to die. Why did she die? She was getting better, you said so. What happened?'

So Jill, stifling her anger at his part in Helen's death, explained again and then spent a long time with him that morning talking to him and letting him pour out his feelings. Gradually her inner anger faded and she began to feel sorry for him. He wasn't malicious or hard-headed, like a lot of kids, just bored and looking for kicks. There was no real wickedness in him, and he had been shocked enough by Helen's injuries without having to carry the burden of her death.

She spoke to Zach later about him.

'I imagine the police will throw the book at him,' she said.

He nodded. 'I expect so. Causing death by dangerous driving, driving without a licence; driving without insurance—the list is endless.'

'Do you think they'll send him to prison?'

'He's too young. They have penal detention centres for youths, don't they? Places like Hollesley Bay on the coast. I expect he'll end up there, and his life will be ruined and his parents will be devastated and Helen's parents will be devastated and it's just a colossal bloody mess.'

He sighed and rammed his hands through his hair, and Jill couldn't think of anything to say to make either of them feel better because he was right—it was a dreadful mess and nothing would make it come right. Only time would take the edge off it for any of them.

'His parents live opposite Helen's parents, don't they?'

'I believe so. Another problem to deal with. Oh, well, we can't fix everything, Jilly.' His smile was strained, and he looked tired as she had never seen him, as if his spirit was tired.

All his sparkle was gone.

They struggled through the rest of that wretched day, and at the end they went their separate ways. Jill needed space, and she guessed that Zach did too—sleep as well, and if they were together they wouldn't sleep and that, too, would seem wrong with Helen lying dead in the hospital mortuary.

A pall hung over the ward for days. Steve retreated into himself, and even Jason Bridger couldn't get any reaction from him. He was now up and about a little in a wheelchair, and he made it clear that he was more than ready to go home. His pillion passenger had fortunately made a full recovery, but it was only by the grace of God that he wasn't in the same position as Steve and Jill was sure he felt that keenly.

For Jill and Zach it was another hectic week. He spent a day in Cambridge as part of his higher surgical training, and Jill was appalled at how much she missed him.

Not that there was time to mope. They had a steady stream of patients for operation, many of them hip and knee replacements with a rapid turnover and needing intensive attention for the few days they were in. On top of that there were several emergency admissions, nothing nasty but just enough to keep the nursing staff running flat out, and it couldn't have come at a better time.

Gradually, with the change of patients and the lapse of time, the sadness that had suffused the ward at the beginning of the week faded to a gentle regret, and then moved on. Helen was put out of their minds as they all got on with the business of getting well again.

By the weekend, Jill and Zach were both ready to throw off their doom and gloom. Their relationship, so recently become intimate, demanded their attention again. Zach was on call but, even so, they managed to spend time together.

They finished flooring the upstairs of the barn, and Jill was relieved that the builder had been in and fixed the banisters during the week.

She now felt safer upstairs, which was just as well as they spent a considerable amount of time exploring each other's responses in the newly-created bedroom. They tried things that a couple of weeks ago would have made Jill's hair curl just to think about, but together and in context they seemed absolutely right and unbelievably good.

For the most part. Sometimes things didn't go according to plan and then Jill discovered Zach's outrageous sense of humour and irrepressible good nature.

She had fun. Masses of fun, and she felt as if she'd known him for years and years and years.

They started the new week refreshed, although they shouldn't have done by rights. They hadn't devoted much time to sleep, but the sleep they'd had must have been deep and cleansing because Jill felt that she could tackle the world.

Zach, too, seemed to be in wonderful spirits. He was flirting again, she noticed, and she discovered that she was jealous. That upset her because it marred their relationship, but she knew in her heart of hearts that it was just a harmless bit of fun and designed to keep the old ladies happy.

It didn't keep her happy, though, and she didn't know quite how to deal with it. It ate away at her over the next few days, and she became more and more withdrawn. Every touch, every gesture directed at someone other than her seemed to assume monumental proportions, until she thought she'd scream if she saw him smile at yet another patient. She didn't understand herself and at night, when they were alone, she was quiet and uncommunicative, coming alive only when he took her in his arms and made love to her.

Then she became demanding, as if her body clamoured for his exclusive attention, and their love-making became even more intense. Then, back on the ward, her eyes would follow him again and her heart would contract every time she heard him laugh.

On Friday morning things came to a head. She was just going to snatch a cup of coffee in a rare moment of quiet when she saw Zach with an elderly patient. She was going home after a protracted recovery from her hip replacement, and as she was about to be wheeled out by her daughter she reached up and pulled him down then hugged him.

He laughed, pulled away a little then bent and kissed her forehead. He said something that made them all laugh and then straightened up to see them off with a wave, just as Jill, her face frozen, turned away.

Zach, predictably, noticed and followed her into the ward kitchen.

'What's wrong, precious? You look mad about something.'

'Do I?' she said with pretended indifference.

'Yes.' He snagged her chin with his finger and turned her to face him. 'You do. What's eating you?'

She couldn't meet his eyes. She didn't want to feel angry with him but she did, and it would spoil everything.

'Jilly?' he pushed.

'You just don't know how to behave, do you? You can't seem to get through the day without touching everyone and flirting with them.'

'What?' He dropped his hand and she looked up at him, amazed to see the stunned look on his face.

'You don't have to look so innocent. You know you're doing it.'

'Flirting with who?' he said in what sounded like genuine confusion.

'The old dears. You always do it. They lap it up. Take Mrs Jennings there.'

'What about her?'

'You hugged her.'

'So? And, anyway, she hugged me.'

'And you kissed her,' Jill continued.

'She asked me to.'

'So you had to do it?'

He sighed impatiently. 'Jill, she's seventy-six! How the hell can you make something of that?'

Put like that it did sound silly, but it was hard to backtrack. She qualified it. 'You do it all the time, with everyone. Every time I hear laughter on the ward you're there in the middle of it with your glib tongue and your come-to-bed eyes, turning them inside out with your flattery.'

'I just chat to them,' he protested. 'For God's sake, Jill, don't tell me you're jealous of a few old bats with fifty years on you!'

She turned away. Was she really being unreasonable? 'It's just the way you do it, without even noticing. It's like breathing. You just—it's just the way you are.'

'I thought you liked me the way I am,' he said softly.

'I do—but only with me.'

'So I have to be a different person with everybody else? Jill, that's ridiculous. I'm me—'

'Yes—a flirt. A womaniser. I always knew it.'

He sighed sharply, and she heard the door open. 'This is ridiculous, Jill. I haven't got time for it. It all boils down to trust again, doesn't it? If you're jealous of the old ladies, what the hell will you be like if I smile at a woman of child-bearing age?'

It was a sobering thought and one he left her with, striding out of the room and leaving the ward with a face like thunder.

'What's eating him?' Mary O'Brien asked, coming into the kitchen a moment later.

Jill couldn't answer. It just seemed so silly.

'Sorry, is it personal?' Mary apologised.

She sighed shortly. 'He kissed Mrs Jennings goodbye and I overreacted.'

Mary looked at her curiously. 'Why?'

'Why did I overreact?' She shrugged. 'He's always doing things like that.'

'And you're jealous?'

Slowly, she nodded. 'Yes. He says it's ridiculous.'

'And so it is. You're being silly, Jill. He's a warm, open, friendly sort of person. He talks to people. He's a toucher, too. Are you going to let it upset you every time he does it?'

'Probably,' she admitted.

Mary plugged the kettle in and turned to face her again. 'Well, you've got a problem, then, haven't you, because you won't change him. People don't, you know. That's why so many marriages founder on the rocks—unrealistic expectations.' Mary shot her a keen look. 'You love him, don't you?'

She nodded miserably. 'Yes. I suppose that's why it

hurts to see him doing things with other people that he does with me. It stops it being special.'

'And you need to be special to him?'

She nodded again, wretchedly aware of how dependent she had become on him for her happiness.

'Has he told you he loves you?'

'No.'

'He will—and as for doing special things with you, I'm sure if you think about it there are lots of things he does with you he wouldn't dream of doing with other people. If you can't think of any you're either incredibly dense or your relationship hasn't progressed the way I thought it had.'

Jill gave a strained little laugh. 'Oh, it has. And you're right, of course. He is different with me in many ways. It's just that when I see other people making him laugh I feel jealous because it's *my* job to make him laugh.'

Mary sighed. 'You can't keep him in a glass case, sweetheart. He needs light and air and other people. He's laughing because he's happy inside, and you've done that to him. Can't you just watch him and be glad that you've made him happy?'

It all made so much sense. All she had to do was put it into practice, and Zach, of course, was far from happy the next time she saw him.

She was too busy to find time to talk to him, though, because they had had a new emergency admission, a man with a crushed foot who was waiting for surgery and possible amputation. Zach was called back to the ward from a clinic to check him, and she found herself working beside him in a fraught silence that didn't bode well for their continuing relationship.

He explained to Mr Gilroy and his wife what they hoped to achieve in Theatre, explained that should it be necessary

they would need to amputate his foot, instructed Jill to get
the consent form signed and nodding curtly to her he went
out without another word.

Jill completed the admission procedure, checked Mr
Gilroy's vital signs again and asked him if he understood
the nature of his operation. Then, having got a signature
on the consent form she went back to the workstation.

Zach was there, on the phone to Theatre, booking a
space for the operation.

'We're going up at three-thirty,' he told Jill economi-
cally. 'Make sure he's ready, please.'

'Yes, sir,' she muttered.

He swore under his breath and strode off, leaving her
feeling miserable and alone.

Behind her Mary tsked. 'You two still fighting?' she
said mildly.

'I feel so stupid,' Jill told her wretchedly. 'I want to
apologise and he just won't give me an inch.'

'He's busy,' Mary said comfortingly. 'Go and see him
tonight and tell him you're sorry, and make it up.'

'He'll probably set the dog on me.'

Mary laughed. 'Not Zach. He'll welcome you with
open arms.'

He didn't. Well, not at first. He made her work for his
forgiveness.

She stood in the doorway, her hands twisting each other
into knots, and dragged in a deep breath. 'I'm sorry,' she
forced out. 'I'm being silly, I know. It's just got out of
proportion.'

'It certainly has.'

He didn't say anything else; didn't invite her in; didn't
soften even a little.

She swallowed. Damn, he was going to make this as hard as possible. 'I don't mean to be possessive.'

'I don't mind you being possessive. I like being possessed by you. I just don't like it when you accuse me of doing things I haven't done. I don't flirt. I don't tease and wind people up and make sexual inuendoes and carry on like that. I wouldn't. It's unethical and irresponsible, and it makes me livid that you think I would. I can't help it if the ladies flirt with me, though. Perhaps you'd better make me a badge that says, "Hands off my man"—except that you'd have to make a commitment yourself then, wouldn't you, and you won't do that?'

Her eyes flew up to meet his. 'What do you mean?'

He sighed. 'I mean you'd have to open up to me and let me inside—share your heart with me. You don't, you know. You keep me firmly at a distance.'

'That's crazy,' she whispered. 'We make love—'

He laughed. 'You think because we make love that means we don't have to talk? We don't have to open up to each other and share things? Hopes, fears, dreams—especially fears. Fears are hard to share, aren't they? So we don't. I'm guilty of it, too, but at least I'm not deluded by our physical relationship. Just because you'll let me close to you physically doesn't mean you've let me near you on an emotional level.'

She couldn't look into his eyes any longer because he seemed to be able to see right inside her, and everything he'd said was true.

She bit her lip. 'I want to,' she said unhappily. 'Zach, I'm just afraid.'

'Don't be,' he coaxed and, releasing the edge of the door, he pulled her gently into the house and his arms.

She fell against him, the tears welling up from the morass of unhappinesss seething within her, and his large, firm hand cupped the back of her head and cradled it in the hollow of his shoulder. She could feel his lips on her hair, and she turned her face blindly up to him and kissed him.

'I'm sorry,' she whispered raggedly. 'It's just that I find it so hard to trust. I know I'm being silly.'

He hugged her gently. 'If you'd only trust me with your feelings you'd realise you were safe, sweetheart. I'll never hurt you.'

He sounded so believable. There just seemed to be so much at stake. She'd got in so deep with him without realising—without having the slightest idea of how much she could love or how much it would mean.

Could she trust him?

It was still only a maybe, but she'd have to try. . .

CHAPTER SEVEN

JILL would have liked to have spent the weekend with Zach trying to repair the damage she had caused by her overreaction. However, she was on duty, and so on Saturday morning she eased herself reluctantly out of his arms and left him sleeping peacefully.

She went home, showered and changed into her uniform and went to work. She took the report from the night sister, despatched her staff to work and went to see Mr Gilroy, the man who in the end had unfortunately lost his foot.

He was very heavily sedated still, and she had just a brief chat with him before turning back the bedclothes over the cradle and checking that the wound wasn't bleeding unduly and that the suction drain was working. All seemed well and so she covered him up again, happy that the nurse sitting with him was aware of the possible complications of his operation and was on the lookout for them.

'He probably won't talk too much for a while,' she said quietly to the young woman. 'Just make sure he seems comfortable—do his mouth if he wants and give him a little wash, and make sure his pillows are comfy. I'm not sure if it's sunk in that he's lost his foot, so be prepared for any questions.'

'What do I tell him?'

'Nothing. Tell him a doctor will be round to see him soon and will tell him all about it, and come and tell me. We'll get the duty doctor to have a chat.'

She went back out into the main ward and left the

girl, a final-year student, with her patient. She seemed intelligent enough and hopefully would be able to deal with the situation, but with the more theoretical training nurses were receiving now Jill wasn't convinced that she would have enough clinic experience to handle a really tricky situation if it arose.

Still, she wasn't alone. Jill was around, and a qualified staff nurse, so it wasn't as if she had to struggle unsupported.

Unfortunately, Jill's optimism was unfounded. The young nurse, in floods of tears, came and found her as she was doing the drugs at ten o'clock.

'He's gone crazy,' she wept. 'He said he didn't give permission for his foot to be amputated and he wants to see you now, and the doctor who did it, and he's really mad, and I'm so sorry. I didn't mean to tell him, I just blurted it out—'

'Hush, hush, it's not your fault,' Jill soothed, and led the girl into her office. 'Tell me again—what happened, exactly?'

She sniffed. 'He said his foot hurt, and he wanted to know what had been done. I told him the doctor would come and discuss it with him and he said if he'd known it would hurt this much he would have had it amputated because then it wouldn't hurt, and I said that wasn't true— it still would hurt.'

'You didn't tell him?'

She shook her head. 'No—not then. Anyway, he said the bandage was too tight over his toes and could I loosen it, and I said no, he'd have to see the doctor, and then he said he'd loosen it and I said he mustn't because there was a drain in the stump—and that was it, really. It was the word stump that set him off.'

'Oh. Right, well, don't worry. I'll go and speak to him.'

'He wants to see Dr Samuels.'

So do I, Jill thought, but suppressed the urge to ring him just to hear the sound of his voice. 'He's not on duty this weekend.'

'He's pretty adamant.'

Jill smiled. 'I can handle him. You go and wash your face and have a cup of coffee, then I'll find something else for you to do.'

She went and found the staff nurse, locked up the drugs trolley and went to see Mr Gilroy, who was lying in his room yelling his head off for attention. He was, as the nurse had said, very upset and demanding, and clearly in a state of shock.

'Shh, Mr Gilroy, come on, settle down. It's all right—'

'All right? Are you mad, girl? That lunatic's taken my foot off!' he raved. 'I never said he could do that!'

'Mr Gilroy, please, calm down and try and relax. I've called for a doctor to come and talk to you, but you mustn't allow yourself to get in such a state—'

'State? I'll get in a state if I want! He's taken my bloody foot off!'

Jill sat on a chair by the bed and captured his flailing hand. 'Mr Gilroy, it was destroyed. There was no possibility of saving it. The blood and nerve supplies had been severed—'

He yanked his hand out of hers. 'They sew feet back on—damn, they sew whole legs back on!'

'Only if the severed part is intact, and it's not usually outstandingly successful. Your foot was by no means intact. I'll get the doctor who admitted you to show you the X-rays so you can see the damage, but I can assure you it was considerable. They wouldn't have removed it without very good cause. Anyway, all this was explained to you. I thought you understood. You discussed it both with me and Dr Samuels, and your wife was here too. She'll tell you—you did agree to it, if it proved to be absolutely necessary.'

'I don't believe you. I want to see this Dr Samuels— now! And I want my wife.'

'I'll call her,' Jill promised, 'but I'm afraid Dr Samuels isn't on duty this weekend.'

'So get him off his bloody golf course or out of his boat and back in here to talk to me. He's crippled me for life—he needn't think he's going to sit on his backside and get away with it! I'll see him in court first!'

Jill sighed. 'Very well,' she said quietly. 'I'll call him and tell him you want to see him. Whether or not he's able to come in is a different matter.'

She went out of the room, sent the staff nurse in to sit with him and called Zach.

'Gilroy wants your blood,' she said without preamble. 'Says you didn't have permission to take his foot off and he's talking major repercussions—probably legal action.'

Zach swore. 'I've got the electrician due here in ten minutes—I'll just get him started and I'll come over.'

'Don't hurry,' Jill advised. 'It's just that he's got denial in a bad way. I'll see if I can talk him through it, and I'll get his wife in. She was there when we discussed it. I'll see you later.'

She hung up and called Mrs Gilroy, and explained that her husband had just learned that his foot had been amputated and was very upset.

'Oh, dear,' she sighed. 'I was afraid this would happen. Should I come in?'

'If you wouldn't mind. I know we said to stay away this morning to give him time to recover, but he's getting himself in an awful state and if you can calm him down I think it would be a good idea.'

The woman promised to come in immediately and Jill
went to finish the drugs round with the staff nurse, sending
the miserable student back in with Mr Gilroy for the
time being.

'I'm so sorry,' she said again to Jill, but Jill patted her
arm soothingly.

'Don't worry, love, it isn't your fault. He had to know
sooner or later.'

'I just feel so guilty.'

'Don't. He's just going to have to face it, and some
people find it terribly difficult. We'll give him a sedative
in a while and maybe that will help him calm down before
he does himself a mischief. We're just waiting for the
SHO to come up.'

In the end Zach arrived just after Mrs Gilroy and before
the other doctor. He went in with Mr and Mrs Gilroy on
his own, and came out some twenty minutes later looking
thoroughly disgruntled. 'He won't listen,' he said. 'He
reckons his wife's lying; she ought to know better; she's
covering up for me; he should have been asked about it
before it was removed; she's forged his signature on the
document—you name it. He just can't remember signing
it and won't believe he did.'

Jill chewed her lip. 'Does that put us in a difficult legal
situation?'

He shrugged. 'It might. I tell you what, I'll call the boss
and ruin his weekend too. Perhaps he'll have a magic cure.'

Jill doubted it. Some patients were just unable to come
to terms easily with the reality of amputation, even when
it was expected and planned for. Out of the blue, like Mr
Gilroy's, it could be very traumatic for them and some
found the only way to deal with the shock of their loss
was to blame other people. If they managed to convince
him that it wasn't a case of hospital negligence, then the

focus of his anger would no doubt shift to the person who had caused the accident.

Jill wished them luck. She could still hear Gilroy from the other end of the ward.

Robert Ryder was at home, and told Zach he'd come straight in and that he'd better have his facts checked and the paperwork in order or he'd be for the high jump.

'Well, at least we both know that consent form was signed by him in front of witnesses and with his full understanding.'

'Did he understand, though? I went through it with him again to make sure and he seemed to be aware of what I was asking him to agree to, but perhaps he wasn't.'

'Whatever. I know the foot couldn't have been saved. I know he would have died had we left the leg without surgical intervention—I've got no qualms about my professional part in all this, or yours.'

Jill grinned weakly. 'I'm glad you've got so much faith.'

'We haven't done anything wrong, Jill. We followed the book to the letter. Just because he now can't remember signing the form doesn't mean that he didn't do so in a clear and lucid state of mind. He understood what we were saying, but I think he didn't realise how likely it was that he would lose the foot. Incidentally, talking of not remembering things, did you wake me this morning before you sneaked out of bed?' he added in an undertone, his eyes sparkling with wickedness.

Her smile was soft and all woman. 'No. I didn't like to—you'd only just gone back to sleep.'

'Hmm. In which case,' he murmured, 'I could have a kiss good-morning, really, couldn't I?'

Jill's eyes widened. 'Here? Now?'

He chuckled. 'Perhaps not standing in the middle of the ward. How about the office?'

'How about later, at home?'

'But it won't be the morning.'

'Shame. You'll have to have two—'

'Two what?'

Zach turned to his boss and wiped the smile off his face. 'Nothing. I'm glad you're here. What do you want to do first—see the patient or look at the paperwork?'

'Paperwork, definitely. I'm not going in there to defend you without ammunition.'

So he was taken into the office and shown the consent form, the A and E report, the X-rays, the clinic notes taken on his admission—anything that might be relevant. After scanning it all he leant back, regarded Zach steadily and nodded. 'OK. You did it all right. I've got no qualms about that. Now, how do we convince Mr Gilroy?'

Zach gave a hollow laugh. 'Search me. He thinks I'm an axe murderer.'

Robert Ryder sighed and got to his feet. 'OK. I'll go and talk to him, and see if I can get any sense out of him myself.'

'And I,' Zach said quietly, closing the door, 'will get my kiss good-morning.'

Jill protested, but not a great deal. She was actually quite happy to be drawn into his arms and kissed until her blood hummed in her veins.

Happy, that is, until Robert Ryder came back into the room.

'I shouldn't celebrate your escape from legal action quite yet,' he said drily, and, picking up the file from the desk, he went out again—shutting the door with a quiet click.

'Oops,' Zach said with a grin. 'Let's hope he's broad-minded.'

Jill chuckled. 'The way your luck's going, no chance.'

He was, however. At least, he said no more about it when he came to find them a little while later. Jill was working on the hated computer, and Zach was standing behind her leaning across to guide her fingers and demonstrate various functions that she found incomprehensible. He straightened up and smiled tentatively.

'Well?'

'I think you'll be all right. He's still angry, but he's beginning to realise that the foot was destined to come off whether he gave permission before or not, just to save his life. I've piled it on a little about bleeding to death and gangrene and so forth, and I think he'll calm down. He's mostly just shocked because, of course, it was very sudden. Oh, well. If you two don't have any further plans to disrupt my weekend I'll go and get on with the decorating, or I won't have finished the nursery before the baby goes to school.'

'I thought it wasn't due yet,' Jill said with a frown.

He laughed. 'It isn't. It's just taking me a long time to paint the room!'

They chuckled and watched him go, then Zach turned to her. 'So I'm off the hook—he thinks.'

'I should hope so. You haven't done anything wrong.'

He pursed his lips for a moment. 'That young nurse—what's her name?'

'Angela?'

'Mmm. Where is she? I could do with a word.'

Jill straightened. 'What about?'

He searched her eyes. 'I don't want her feeling guilty, that's all. I was just going to reassure her.'

Jill relaxed a little. 'Oh. I didn't want you telling her off.'

'Why not?'

'Because that's my job and, rest assured, I shall be doing it.'

'Oh.' He grinned. 'Poor Angela. Don't be hard on her.'

Jill sighed. 'I won't, but she shouldn't have done what she did.'

'It was an honest mistake,' Zach reminded her.

'I know. You go and reassure her and mend fences with Mr Gilroy, and I'll finish putting this lot into the computer and try and keep my cool before I forget what you told me.'

It was probably the computer's fault but just when Jill was at her most frustrated she saw Zach with Angela, gazing awestruck up into his dangerously beautiful eyes, and she wanted to kill.

Then he laughed softly and chucked her under the chin, and Jill had to breathe deeply and tell herself that it was just his way and it meant nothing and it wasn't his fault the girl looked like a lovesick calf. Even so, when he wandered over and gave her the same warm, loving grin she wanted to scream and rant and wipe it off his face.

You're mine, she wanted to say. Don't smile at other women!

Then he leant over her and said, 'I think I have problems with Angela. She looks at me as if she'd like to eat me, and I couldn't be less interested. I'm too busy wanting you.'

'I'm glad to hear it,' she murmured, her temper easing.

His grin widened. 'Do you know what I want to do? I want to get that zip and slide it down and reach inside your dress and find those delectable, soft little breasts and suckle them until you can't see straight.'

She gasped and blushed slightly. 'Zach, for heaven's sake, someone will hear you!' she muttered furiously, trying not to laugh.

'Do you know what I want to do then? I want to slide my hand up that beautiful, smooth thigh—'

'How would you like to go home before you embarrass us both so badly we can't work here any longer?' she muttered through clenched teeth, wondering if anyone had noticed her rising colour.

He laughed and straightened. 'If you insist. Come over when you finish. That rudely interrupted kiss has left me hungry.'

And he went, leaving Angela gaping at Jill in open-mouthed curiosity. How to handle that? she wondered. Blush and run, or confront her? Grabbing her courage in both hands, she raised an eyebrow and stared her junior down.

It wasn't subtle, but it worked. Angela went scarlet, retreated into her shell and was the model of hard work and efficiency for the rest of the day.

And Zach, when she arrived back at the barn in her uniform some five hours later, followed through on his promises with considerable style and panache. They ended up in the shower together, which would have been a great deal less embarrassing if Ryan O'Connor hadn't arrived just as they were coming back down to earth.

'Sorry, I'll go,' he said with genuine apology, but he looked so sad and left out and lonely that Jill wanted to hug him.

'No,' she said, 'please stay. Have supper with us,' which earned her a wry grin from Zach a moment later when Ryan's back was turned.

He blew her a kiss, though, so she assumed she was forgiven. She didn't care if she wasn't, really. She couldn't forget how readily Ryan had opened his home to them in the few days following the drama of Brian Birkett's shooting spree, and if he was lonely and needed company, well, they had plenty of time to be alone together.

Zach found some salad in the fridge and they grilled

some sausages on the gas barbeque and then lay around on the patio in the late afternoon sun, drinking the contents of a bottle of wine Ryan had produced and talking about the problem with Mr Gilroy, and the progress on the barn, and Mrs Birkett's slow-to-heal foot.

Jill studied Ryan as he talked, and wondered again how his wife had died and how long ago. Poor man, he was so much alone, living in a strange country because it had been his wife's home and the children's only other relatives were here. How could she regret sharing this evening with him? When Ryan left them at about midnight she spoke to Zach about it while they cleared away the supper things.

'I'm sorry I asked him to stay without consulting you, but he looked so sad and he was so kind to us.'

'I know. I didn't really mind. I was just looking forward to having you to myself. I missed you.'

She smiled. 'I missed you, too. It seemed odd on the ward without you popping in.' She put the glasses down in the kitchen sink. 'Zach, how did his wife die?'

'Car accident,' he told her. 'About two years ago, I think. The children were in the car with them, and he was asleep. Ann was driving, and a drunk driver came out of nowhere and smashed straight into the driver's side. She was killed instantly.'

Jill, wondering how she would feel if that had been Zach, shuddered and put her arms round him. 'How dreadful,' she muttered into his shirt front. 'Fancy losing so much so fast, without any warning.'

'I don't know that warning would have helped. The feelings still have to be gone through.'

'But not being able to say goodbye—'

She buried her face in his chest and held on tight.

'Hey,' he said softly and, easing her away he, tipped

her chin up and looked down into her damp eyes. As he watched they overflowed, and he bent and kissed away her tears. 'Oh, sweetheart,' he murmured. 'Come on, let's go to bed. I want to hold you.'

They made love very tenderly that night, without any words or laughter or reckless haste, and afterwards Jill clung to his broad chest and imagined him lying cold in a mortuary and hoped desperately that she died with him so that neither of them ever had to endure such a terrible loss. . .

After that their relationship seemed to take on a greater depth. Zach tried to understand her feelings about the way he interacted with other people, and often now would share the joke with her afterwards or wink at her if one of the ladies tried to chat him up.

One woman became a serious embarrassment and he had to enrol Jill's protection. 'Come with me,' he would mutter, and all but drag her along at his side if he had to talk to the patient.

And then, for the first time, Jill realised that he actually had to say nothing provocative at all because his looks and smile and eyes were enough to make women lose their reason.

She only had to look at herself! She was a prime example.

And so she began to relax and allow him his social banter, and the difference in her attitude had a reflection in his, too. He began to share more of his feelings with her, and talked about his training and his ambitions and aspirations, and his worries and weaknesses.

Jill still found it hard to open herself too much to him, though. Just loving him was enough to make her realise how dependent she was on him for the very air she breathed, and the thought of laying herself open to hurt was terrifying.

So she kept a little something back and if Zach was hurt by it he didn't say so, just gently encouraged her when she did inadvertently reveal more of the layers of her personality.

She found that he was willing to share his fears, though—like the fear that Mr Gilroy would take him to court for the amputation of his foot, even though nothing more had been said in the intervening week.

'But he signed the form! He was quite lucid—it was just shock and the sense of loss that made him so unreasonable,' Jill argued.

'Even so, he might take me to court—or at least the hospital—and it could smash my chances of promotion when I finish my training.'

'No way,' she said confidently. 'He won't and, anyway, it wouldn't affect your chances. You're much too good. Robert Ryder speaks very highly of you.'

He flushed—he actually flushed; and Jill hugged him, delighted by his modesty. 'You are good,' she went on, to reinforce the point. 'All the patients love you.'

'I thought you hated that?' he said quizzically.

'Only when I didn't understand. Anyway, I fell for those baby blues. Why shouldn't they?'

He grinned wickedly. 'Because I never look at the patients the way I look at you,' he said.

'That's just as well—you'd be arrested!' she teased.

'Anyway,' he went on, tucking her into his side on the sofa and propping his feet up on the old box that passed as a coffee table, 'what makes you think Gilroy won't do anything now?'

'He said so,' she told him. 'This afternoon, in fact. He told me he'd just overreacted because he never really believed you would need to amputate it. When he woke up and realised it was gone, he was devastated.'

'I noticed,' Zach said drily.

'How would you feel, though, if it was you?' she pointed out fairly. 'It must be the most dreadful shock. One minute you're fine; the next you're crippled for life. Dreadful. Still, he's getting on well now. They're going to start him walking with the PPAM aid this week.'

'I often wonder whether walking round on a pneumatic gadget that looks so unlike a leg can possibly be good for their egos, but the physios all seem to think it is.'

'I think it's just the fact of being vertical again. Spending too long lying down is so bad for you, and crutches are difficult to manage—if you can get your weight down through both legs in an almost normal way, it must make you feel better.'

'Provided you don't look down and see the plastic bag and metal frame, of course.'

Jill shrugged. 'Perhaps that's all part of acceptance. At least the legs are a damn sight better now. Did you know we used to have a registrar here who was an amputee? Michael Barrington, his name was. I was just a staff nurse at the time on A and E, and I remember when he was brought in. He'd got his leg trapped in a train, treating someone after a derailment, and they'd had to amputate his foot to get him out. It was terrible—we were all so shocked. He'd just got engaged at the time and his fiancée was with him.'

'Pity he's not still here. What happened to him; did he give up?'

'Michael?' She laughed. 'No. He and Clare sailed the Atlantic. He's a consultant now in Ipswich, and they've got two children at the last count. He was a great guy. Nick Davidson's his successor.'

'He's off to a consultancy too, I understand.'

'They all go, the rising young stars. I suppose you will, too.'

'Not for a consultancy—not for at least three years, anyway. I may have to go to Norwich or Cambridge, though, for a year.'

She felt suddenly very vulnerable. Would they still be together after that time? And if so, would he want her to go with him?

She felt his finger under her chin, turning her face round towards him. His arm was still round her shoulders and it eased her closer as his head came down. 'Don't be scared, Jilly. I won't leave you,' he murmured against her lips.

Did he mean it? Was it a commitment? He still hadn't told her that he loved her. Perhaps he didn't. Perhaps he was just sweet-talking.

His mouth touched hers, and suddenly she didn't care. Whenever they were parted would be too soon. For now, though, she had him and she didn't intend to waste a single moment. . .

CHAPTER EIGHT

ZACH was at a loss. No matter how much he coaxed, Jill wouldn't open up to him and give him any inkling of her feelings. There were times—mainly in bed—when he felt that she was on the verge of telling him she cared, but she never did. Perhaps that was why he hadn't, either.

Unsure how to proceed, restless and unhappy, he called Ryan. Jill was on late and wasn't coming over, and the evening stretched ahead of him like a yawning void. Perhaps his friend fancied a game of squash? He could only ask.

Ryan answered the phone quickly, as if he had been sitting beside it.

'Are you waiting for a call?' Zach said immediately, not wishing to hold up the line if he was.

'No—just sitting at my desk going through a few papers. What can I do for you?'

Zach sighed. 'How about a brain transplant?'

Ryan chuckled. 'That good, eh?'

'At least. I don't suppose there's a chance you could get a babysitter so we could play squash?'

'Tonight?'

'If possible.'

'Yeah, I don't see why not. My neighbour's daughter is always strapped for cash—I'm sure she'd come over. I'll ring her and call you back. Why don't you go ahead and book a court anyway?'

Half an hour later they were on the court, and Zach was thrashing out his frustration and restlessness. After a few

minutes Ryan, smashing into the wall in a vain attempt to
return yet another really fast shot, turned and propped his
hips against the wall, rested his hands on his knees and
peered up at Zach.

'Something eating you?' he panted.

Zach grinned, propped himself against the opposite wall
and dragged the back of his hand over his streaming
forehead.

'Me?' he said innocently.

Ryan straightened. 'You, damn your black heart. You're
killing me.'

Zach gave a hollow laugh. 'Sorry. It's just. . .' He ran
out of words, shaking his head and sighing.

'Jill?' Ryan offered.

Zach nodded. 'Yeah.'

'Want to talk about it?'

He grunted and smashed the ball into the front wall
with vigour. Ryan let it go and Zach met his eyes, picked
up the ball and grinned wryly. 'Sorry. Let's play, huh?
We'll talk later.'

'Will I survive?' Ryan asked mildly.

Zach flung an arm over his friend's shoulders and
hugged him briefly. 'I'll see if I feel generous.'

With the edge taken off his frustration, and with Ryan
forwarned this time, Zach found himself thrashed. He
forced himself to concentrate and won the next game, then
lost the following to Ryan. Finally they called a halt, both
hot and sweating freely and breathing hard.

'I think that'll do for cardiovascular exercise for the
night,' Ryan said with a grin. He blew the hair off his
forehead and wiped his eyes on the back of his arm.
'Shower and drink?'

Zach nodded. 'Sounds good.'

They ended up in a riverside pub, sitting outside under

a willow tree with ice-cold fruit juice and a stack of high-cholesterol sandwiches.

'So—what's with you and Jill?' Ryan asked, getting straight to the point.

Zach bit into a sandwich and chewed it thoughtfully, staring out across the river.

'I don't know how she feels about me.'

'So ask her.'

'It's not that easy. She holds back all the time. She'll give me her body but she won't give me her mind. If she would just open up a little I'd know where I stood with her, but I honestly don't have a clue.'

'Have you told her how you feel?'

Zach shook his head. 'No.'

'So maybe she feels the same way?'

'Maybe.'

Ryan took a long swallow of his fruit juice, picked up another sandwich and opened it, removing the cucumber. 'Maybe you need to tell her how you feel—lead the way. Make her realise that she's important to you—I take it she is?'

Zach gave a short, humourless laugh. 'Oh, yes. Hell, yes. She's taken over my life. Everything I do, I find I'm considering her. The wall colour, for instance. She said she likes yellow in kitchens, so guess what colour the kitchen walls are going to be? She asked if I was putting a bidet in the bathroom. It hadn't even occurred to me, but there's one on order now. I'm doing the house for her, Ryan, and I don't even know if she's going to be sharing it with me.'

He threw the remains of his sandwich into the river and watched the ducks attack it. 'I love her, Ryan. I think I'm afraid to tell her that in case it isn't what she wants to hear.'

Ryan was silent for a minute, chewing thoughfully, then

he lounged back against the bench and stretched his long legs out and gazed up at the tree. 'I can't tell you what to do,' he said slowly. 'If it was me, I'd tell her. I'd have to. I'm no good at keeping my feelings hidden.'

Zach snorted. 'You think I am? It's killing me to give her time, but it's complicated, Ryan. She's been messed about—her first lover turned out to be married with kids, and it really hurt her very deeply. Then Gordon Furlow—'

'That creep!'

'Yeah, well, he got his comeuppance. She chucked coffee over him in the canteen.'

Ryan chuckled. 'I heard. He deserved it, though. He should have ended it with Jill first before he moved on.'

'Maybe he didn't think there was anything to end? Their relationship was pretty tepid, from what I can gather.'

'Even so. I'm sorry I said anything about it now. Perhaps he would have just told her it was over and then gone public with Maria a little while later.'

Zach shook his head. 'I doubt it. He's got about as much finesse as a brick where Jill's concerned. He sent her flowers from him and Maria, telling Jill he'd decided to forgive her for humiliating him.'

Ryan doubled up with laughter. 'He did what? Oh, man, that is priceless! What did she say?'

Zach chuckled. 'They went in the bin.'

'Good for her.'

'The trouble is,' Zach went on, 'she's had a rough time in the fidelity stakes and she doesn't give her trust easily. That's why I've tried not to rush her. I didn't want her to think I was insincere.'

'But you're not.'

'No. I want to marry her, Ryan. I want to grow old with her. Does that sound hopelessly romantic?'

Ryan's face grew grave and still. 'No. No, it doesn't

sound hopelessly romantic at all. It sounds as if you love her the way I loved Ann.' His voice dropped to a thread. 'I just hope you get the chance.'

Zach gave a shaky sigh. 'God, Ryan, I'm sorry. That was so thoughtless.'

'No, it wasn't. It was honest. It's how you feel. At least I can understand it. Zach, Ann's dead, but I can remember our courtship—the way I felt, the way we carried on. It was wonderful. I don't regret a moment of it, and I'd hate you to feel uncomfortable about it just because Ann's gone now. You can't say anything to me that will make it worse than it already is.'

Zach reached out a hand without thinking and squeezed Ryan's shoulder. There were no words he could say; no action he could take. It made his own worries pale into insignificance.

'Another drink?' he said after a moment.

Ryan shook his head. 'No. It's getting late.'

They walked to the car park, and Ryan stood by Zach's car as he got in. 'I think you should go for it,' he said slowly. 'Tell her how you feel. Maybe it will give her the courage to open up to you. Don't push her, though. Give her time. Let her make the next move.'

Zach nodded. 'Thanks—and thanks for the game.'

Ryan laughed. 'Just warn me next time—I'll get in a little practice first!'

He needed practice, too, Zach decided on the way home. Practice at proposing to Jill. 'I love you, will you marry me?' seemed incredibly straightforward and simplistic. Perhaps it was. Perhaps falling in love was straightforward and simple, like breathing and eating and making love.

Just one of those things people did, he thought, part of the great master plan, a trick to persuade us to procreate and establish stable family bonds to rear our young.

Maybe we made it all unnecessarily complicated.
He decided to talk to Jill the following night.

He was strangely thoughtful, Jill thought, watching Zach
as she twirled her spaghetti round her fork. Distracted,
almost. Was he bored with her? Oh, Lord, no, please.

She put the spaghetti in her mouth and lost a strand,
then flicked her tongue out to retrieve it. Zach, watching
her broodingly across the table, froze for a moment then
reached out with a bit of kitchen roll and blotted her chin.

'How can you make eating spaghetti so sexy?' he
murmured.

She blushed. 'You're nuts.'

His smile was slow but worth waiting for. 'Just eat it
carefully if you want to be allowed to finish it.'

She didn't finish it. They ended up in bed, making long,
slow love all through the mild summer evening, and in
the morning when they came down starving to grab some
breakfast the congealed spaghetti was still clinging to the
plates—the bits that Scud hadn't manage to find.

'You're a thief,' Zach scolded him lovingly.

'Just as well,' Jill said with a grin. 'Someone has to
clear up around here. You need a housemaid.'

Something happened to Zach's eyes, and he took the
plates away from her and put them in the sink then, grabbing two Danish pastries from the fridge, he headed for
the door, Jill in tow.

'Hey! Where are we going?' she asked laughingly as
she trailed behind him, her wrist firmly shackled by his
lean fingers.

'For a walk. Scud? Come, boy.'

He released her and they headed into the woods, munch-
ing the pastries and revelling in the sounds and smells of
the early morning. 'It's wonderful here,' Jill said blissfully.

'How wonderful?' Zach asked carefully.

She looked at him, puzzled by a serious note in his voice.

'Very wonderful,' she replied, just as carefully.

'Do you fancy making it a permanent arrangement?'

She stopped walking and searched his face. 'Permanent? You mean live with you?'

'No, I mean marry me. I love you, Jill. I've loved you for weeks—probably longer. The trouble is, I don't know how you feel about it—about me. You don't ever say anything—' He shrugged. 'I know it isn't easy for you to give commitment. It isn't easy for me, either, but I find with you that's what I want to do. I want to make a commitment. I want—need—you to know that I love you. And I want you to love me back, if you can. If you do.'

She couldn't speak. The words were there, locked in her throat, and the sincerity in his eyes couldn't be doubted. She moved her lips, but no sound came out.

'Oh, Zach,' she managed at last.

'Think about it,' he put in hastily. 'I don't want you to say anything yet. Just let it mull around in your mind—get used to the idea because if you say yes I shall hold you to it, Jilly, make no mistake. I want everything—marriage, kids, fidelity—especially fidelity. You'll be mine for ever. I won't let you go without a fight, and I don't want you if you don't feel the same because it won't work.'

It sounded wonderful. If only she dared.

'Oh, Zach,' she murmured. 'I don't know what to say. Nobody's ever said anything like that to me before.'

'Don't say anything,' he repeated. 'Not now. Not yet. Tomorrow. Give yourself plenty of time to think about it and sleep on it, OK? I've got the electrician coming round again tonight, so we'll wait until tomorrow evening and talk about it then.' He drew her into his arms. 'Just remember that I love you,' he murmured again, and then he kissed her, slowly and thoroughly, before releasing her and turning back towards the barn. 'Come on, we'll be late for work.'

She went with him, her feet working automatically and her heart singing. He loved her. He really did, she was sure of it. And he'd said it was for keeps.

Could she dare to believe in him?

Yes. She could. She'd thought about nothing else all day, even though he'd been too busy to come onto the ward except for the briefest visit. She didn't want to wait until tomorrow. She'd give him her answer tonight.

Now, if he would only come back to the ward and give her thirty seconds alone with him in the office. But he didn't. He was in Theatre all day, generating work for her, and there wasn't really time to think.

One patient for operation that day was a young woman called Debbie Wright, who was in for arthrodesis of the knee following a bad accident. She had had a replacement joint inserted and it had become infected and the bone had started to break down.

The only course of treatment now apart from amputation was to remove the joint and fix the knee. It meant that the leg would be permanently straight, and getting in and out of cars and the bath would be tricky, but at least she would be able to walk again.

Jill spent some time with her prior to her operation, assuring her that she would feel much better when it was done and that although it would always be a slightly strange shape she would at least be out of pain and independently mobile once again.

'I can't wait for that,' Debbie confided. 'I'm so sick of

being on crutches and hurting all the time and not being able to get about. Of course, if I hadn't got my knee smashed in that argument with a car it would have been preferable, but that's the way life goes. I don't suppose there's any chance of them fitting another joint?'

'I shouldn't think so,' Jill told her. 'If there was, I'm sure they would have tried.'

'Might be worth asking,' she said with a grin. 'You never know.'

You never did, Jill thought later, when Debbie came back from Theatre with her knee packed with antibiotic-impregnated acrylic cement, and the possibility of a new joint once the infection had been eradicated. Robert Ryder and Zach had worked together on it after Zach had opened the knee and found that it looked better than he had expected. Robert had agreed with him, and together they had removed the old joint, cleaned up the bone and packed the area with the special cement.

If the infection disappeared they could try a new joint after six to twelve weeks. If not, well, she would be no worse off and she would know that everything possible had been tried.

Jill talked to her when she woke up, after Robert had been down and explained what they had done. She was still drowsy and didn't understand at first, but gradually it dawned on her that there was still hope for her to have a functioning knee joint.

'Great,' she said weakly. 'If it works, that'll be terrific. If it doesn't, what have I lost? A few weeks. That's nothing to pay, is it, for such a chance? Still, I won't build my hopes up.'

Jill thought she was being very philosophical about it, and admired her grit. Debbie was in a lot of pain, and Jill rigged up a pethidine pump so that she could control her own pain relief.

She went home after work, had a bath and washed her hair—combing it out and letting it dry naturally in the sun as she sat in the courtyard garden and sipped a cup of tea. She could have done with a glass of wine, really, to bolster her flagging courage, but she didn't think it was a good idea. Anyway, she didn't have any, so it was academic.

She hoped that the electrician would have been and gone. Otherwise, she thought with a smile, there was a distinct possibility that they'd give the man a bigger shock than the national grid!

She dressed carefully in a clingy, silk-mix dress in palest aqua that she couldn't possibly have worn if she'd had the slightest ripple of fat. It was a bit over the top for a weekday evening but perhaps not too dressy for accepting a proposal of marriage, and it looked lovely with her blonde hair and golden skin. And underneath she wore the lace teddy and nothing else. Why waste time? she thought with a smile.

She hugged herself mentally. Married—and to Zach, of all people! Funny how she'd thought he couldn't handle commitment. She checked her hair and make-up again, gave herself one last twirl in front of the mirror and, grabbing her keys and bag, she set off for the barn.

It was almost dusk, and she could see lights on inside as she came over the hill and down the lane towards the track. He was probably working. After all, he wasn't expecting her, and—

She slammed the brakes on and slithered to a halt just inches from the grinning Scud.

'What are you doing out here on the road? You bad dog!' she scolded lovingly. Then she sniffed. 'Oh, Scud, where have you been? You're filthy!'

She cast about for an idea, but there was only one way to get him home and that was to take him. He wasn't going in her car like that—that was for sure! She pulled the car onto the verge, put the side lights on and locked it. She'd come back for it later—or send Zach. That was the sort of thing a husband did, after all, and it was his dog!

The shoes weren't ideal for the rough, stony track, so she took them off and carried them as she picked her way carefully along it and finally arrived at the barn.

'Damn,' she muttered under her breath. There was a strange car parked beside Zach's. The electrician. Oh, well, she could wait. Scud cocked his leg against one of the wheels and she smiled, then turned towards the barn.

The back door was open and she could hear Zach's voice. Please be getting rid of him, she thought, and then as she reached the open doorway she saw him there, in the hallway beyond the kitchen, but the person with him wasn't the electrician at all—it was a woman. A beautiful woman, her body gently swollen with the middle months of pregnancy, and she was standing in his arms.

Pain shot through her, but she quelled the jealousy. They'd got past that now. There was obviously a logical explanation.

Then the woman spoke, and Jill thought she was going to die.

'Men are all the same,' she said sadly. 'All afraid of commitment, all running from marriage and clinging to their bachelor status—'

'Hey, hang on there,' he interrupted. 'I'm more than ready for marriage!'

'Are you? Well, so am I, and I don't want to be an unmarried mother! It's bad enough being fat and hideous—'

'Hey, hey, hush!' Zach soothed, and his hand—the hand

that had touched her so intimately—stroked the woman's cheek with love and tenderness. 'You're beautiful.'

'I'm fat.'

'No, you're pregnant. That's quite different and, anyway, who the hell wants a stick insect? You're perfect just as you are, and no red-blooded man in his right mind wouldn't agree with me, sweetheart.'

No! Jill wanted to scream. That's what you call me!

The woman was blushing now, and as Jill watched Zach bent and kissed her, oh, so gently, on the mouth. 'As for you being an unmarried mother, I think we should do something about that, don't you?'

Even through her pain Jill could see the hope dawning on the other woman's face. 'Such as?'

Zach grinned, the lopsided, sexy grin he reserved for her—or so she'd thought. 'I think we've got a wedding to arrange. You make some tea—and I'll get on the phone to my brother.'

He kissed her again and Jill, unable to watch another moment, spun on her heel and ran.

The stones cut her bare feet, but she didn't notice. All she wanted to do was escape from Zach and his pregnant woman friend and go home to lick her wounds.

Tears streamed down her face and she stumbled and fell headlong on the gravel, ripping the skin on her hands and knees. She cried out with the pain, the shock holding her there transfixed for a moment, then she scrambled to her feet and limped the last short distance to her car.

She had no idea how she made it home. She shut the door behind her, went into her bedroom and stared blankly at herself in the mirror.

She looked terrible. Her dress, her gorgeous slinky dress, was torn and bloodstained where she had wiped her hands on it. Her legs were streaming with blood, fine trickles running down her shins and over her feet, and her face was streaked with blood and tears.

She felt worse than she looked.

She felt betrayed, desolate, used.

Why had he said all those things to her? Why tell her that he loved her, that he wanted to marry her? Why?

Because it suited him to have her where he wanted her? Or had he thought that the other woman was out of his life and she'd come back unexpectedly?

But he'd told Jill not to go round tonight.

Because he had been expecting the pregnant woman?

Jill unkindly christened her 'Pod'. Had he been expecting Pod all along? Was he one of these men who like to have two strings to his bow?

Jill swallowed the bile that rose in her throat. She'd been there before—twice. Three times now. She laughed. They said that women always went for the same sort of men every time. Did she have to be so predictable?

She wrenched the dress off, then the teddy, ripping the studs off in her frenzy, then stood and looked at herself. 'Who wants a stick insect?' he'd said to Pod.

No hips, no bust—especially no bust. Somebody had once been described as the gable end of a pound note. It fitted her, she thought. Turn sideways and she disappeared.

Had all the things he'd said to her just been platitudes? Maybe he was just desperately unfussy and any body—literally—would have done.

But why her? And why again? She crammed her fist in her mouth, her teeth cutting the taut skin over her knuckles, and trapped the little scream of anguish that rose in her throat.

'Oh, Zach,' she whispered brokenly. 'How could you? I love you—how could you?'

She crumpled there on the hard floor, in front of the

mirror, and stared at her tear-streaked face. Was that really her? It looked like a stranger—a broken, damaged woman with nothing to live for.

A sob rose in her throat, and another, and she fell forwards onto the floor, her arms outstretched—her fingers clawing at the carpet as the violent spasms of grief racked her body.

When the tears were spent she still lay there, naked and bloody, too empty to care if she lived or died. . .

She phoned in sick the following morning. Luckily, Mary was on duty but too busy to talk to her, so she left a message with the staff nurse that she had a cold and crawled into the bath.

The phone rang twice, and later there was pounding on the door, but she didn't move. She couldn't. Nothing seemed to work any more. Nothing except her mind. That was working overtime. She could think of nothing but Zach and how he had betrayed her, and she didn't know where all the tears kept coming from.

She decided in the end, a little hysterically, that she must be siphoning them in from the bath water, so she got out and put on her dressing-gown and made a cup of tea and drank it in the courtyard.

The phoning and pounding seemed to have come to a halt, so perhaps Zach had given up. Maybe he thought she was out.

She went through to her bedroom later and found a note lying on the hall floor. 'Called round to see if you are OK. You must have been out. Ring the ward. Love you, Zach.'

She crushed it in her hand and ignored the fresh batch of tears. Damn him. He could go to hell. He'd find her there, waiting. . .

*   *   *

She rang him later, and they bleeped him in a clinic. That suited her because it meant that he couldn't talk for long or say too much.

'Will you be alone tonight?' she asked.

'I hope not,' he told her. 'I hope you'll be there.'

She ignored the glib, easy words. 'I'll see you at seven,' she said, and hung up before he could ask where she'd been.

Damn, her eyes were leaking again. She'd have to get a grip on herself before tonight or she'd make a complete fool of herself, and the only thing she had left now was her pride.

She dressed soberly that evening. No slinking silk, no lace underwear. Sensible cotton bra and pants, a T-shirt and jeans. You didn't dress up, after all, to tell someone to go to hell.

Anyway, her dress was in the bin.

She arrived at five to seven, impatient to get the difficult and distressing scene over as quickly as possible and get back to her flat to lick her wounds. Zach was outside, sitting on the patio waiting.

He came up to her car with a smile and opened the door, bending to kiss her before she could turn away. 'Hi, sweetheart,' he said lovingly, and she could have hit him.

You called Pod sweetheart, you hypocrite, she wanted to say. Instead she bit the inside of her cheek and got out of the car.

'I dropped round this morning—where were you?'

'I went for a walk,' she lied. 'I wanted to think.'

'I thought you might have done. Come in, let me get you a drink.'

'I'd rather be outside,' she said. She sounded short. She couldn't help it; she couldn't just be all chatty and civilised when her world was falling apart at the seams.

'OK,' he said, and his voice sounded cautious. Good. That would make her job easier. They walked round to the patio, sat down and she started talking without preamble.

'There's no easy way to say this, so I might as well just get it over,' she told him, staring out over the fields. 'I don't love you, Zach—not in the way you need.' Well, that at least was true. He needed a woman who would share him, and she wouldn't. Not with anyone, and most especially not with a pregnant woman who had obviously been with him first. Far be it from her to distract him from his responsibilities. Let Pod have him, and good luck to her.

She went on. 'I can't give you what you want.' That, too, was true. There was no way she could be a part-time lover, not for anyone. Not again.

He was silent for so long that she turned to look at him, and she couldn't divine anything from what she saw.

He was staring at his hands intently, studying them as if he'd never seen them before.

'I see,' he said at last, and his voice sounded rusty and unused. 'So I guess that's it, then?'

'Yes.'

It was that easy. He said he'd bring her things into the ward; she thanked him and stood up; he escorted her to her car and held the door for her, and she drove home.

How polite. How civilised.

How dreadful, that so much could be thrown away in those few short words. . .

CHAPTER NINE

ZACH wasn't surprised—not, at least, by what Jill had said. What did surprise him was the great wave of pain he felt. Letting her go without a fight was perhaps the hardest thing he had ever done, but he'd had to do it. After all, he had to respect her decision, even if it did destroy him—

Damn. He scrubbed the back of his hand over his eyes and dragged in a lungful of air. Then another, and another. Strange. They sounded like sobs.

He bit his lip so hard that he tasted the metallic tang of blood, and gulped down another sob. Hell. He wouldn't cry.

He picked up the phone, stabbing numbers automatically. It was answered on the second ring.

'You busy?' he said without preamble.

'N-o. Not especially.' There was a pause. 'Want to come round?'

'Are the kids in bed?'

'No, they're at their grandparents. Want me to come to you?'

He looked around. Jill's things were everywhere. 'No, I'll come to you.' He dropped the phone back in the cradle and went.

Ryan was at the door before him, opening it without a word and letting him in. 'Inside or out?' he asked.

'In. I need to talk, and I don't want your neighbours listening.'

Ryan led him into the kitchen, pulled out a couple of

cans of beer from the fridge and put them on the table. He handed one to Zach, popped the tab on his and sat down, propping his feet on another chair.

Zach took a couple of long swallows before he sat, elbows on the table, the can dangling from his fingertips.

'She doesn't love me,' he said flatly.

'Ah.'

He sighed. 'I had a feeling she'd say that. I tried to convince myself she loved me, that it was just this business of trust, but perhaps she was holding back because she really didn't love me after all. Perhaps I just wanted her to.' He lifted his head and met Ryan's sympathetic green eyes. 'I thought I was going to die when she left. Then I went back inside and her things are everywhere—'

Ryan swore softly and reached across, shoving another beer towards Zach. 'I know how that feels,' he said quietly. 'Do you want a hand packing all the things up?'

He shook his head. 'No. I'll do it. I'm just being silly. There's not that much.' Underwear in his underwear drawer, wash things in the bathroom, a jumper here and there, a coat for walking the dog, boots— 'I'll cope,' he said heavily.

'So,' Ryan said, leaning back and watching Zach over the top of his can, 'what brought this on?'

'Oh. Of course, you don't know. Yesterday morning I told her I loved her and asked her to marry me. I told her to think about it and sleep on it. This morning she rang in sick, and I went round there but she was out. Her car was there, but she'd gone for a walk. Then she rang me at the hospital and said she'd come over this evening at seven. She sounded a bit strained—short, you know? If she'd been going to say yes I suppose she would have sounded bubbly. She didn't, so I was a bit suspicious then.'

He shoved a hand through his hair impatiently. 'Anyway, she arrived, went straight to the point and told me she didn't love me and couldn't give me what I wanted, and I said so that's it, then, and she said yes. Then she left.'

Ryan's face creased in a frown. 'That's very economical.'

Zach's mouth twitched in a parody of a smile. 'It was just as well. I didn't hold up for too long.'

'That bad, eh?'

Zach swallowed hard and nodded. 'That bad. Then I went back inside and her things were everywhere, like I said, and I just had to get out of there. I'm sorry.'

Ryan smiled sympathetically. 'Don't worry about it. That's what friends are for.'

There was a wuff from outside and Ryan lifted his head. 'Is Scud in the car?'

Zach nodded. 'I didn't like to leave him.'

'Bring him in,' Ryan said. 'He's no trouble.'

So Scud came and leant against Zach's leg, a warm and heavy comfort, his head on Zach's knee, melting brown eyes fixed on his face. He patted the dog and said, 'Good boy,' and then the tears came, great shuddering sobs, and Ryan left him to it and went out to the study.

When he came back he had a bottle of malt whiskey in his hand and he poured a hefty slug and shoved it across the table at Zach.

Zach lifted his head and met Ryan's eyes, and pulled a rueful face. 'Sorry about that. It just hit me.'

'That's OK. It's like that. I understand.'

Zach sighed. 'I don't know why you're being so sympathetic. You should tell me to get the hell out of here and stop being so melodramatic. After all, at least she's still alive. It's not like being bereaved.'

'Isn't it?' Ryan said softly. 'Grief is very largely a selfish emotion, you know. I could tell myself I was sad for Ann because she was missing so much of the kids growing up and all that, but really I was sad for me. She didn't know a damn thing about it. One minute we were driving along; the next she was dead. It was so sudden.'

'I thought you were asleep?'

'I had been. I was still drowsy. I just had time to yell, "Look out!" and the car hit us. She didn't even have time to turn her head. Anyway, that's beside the point. The point is, what I felt and what you're feeling is a sense of loss—an emptiness, something missing where before there was warmth and companionship.

'You're going to be lonely, Zach. You'll fill your days with work and your nights with socialising, and then you'll go home and get into bed and you'll be lonely. That's the hard part.'

'Are you still lonely?'

Ryan's mouth quirked slightly. 'Do birds fly? But I'll do. I've got the kids and they're great, and I've got a whole bunch of colleagues who are pretty good to be with, and I've got you to thrash me at squash every time my ego gets a little inflated.'

Zach chuckled. 'We ought to play again. Perhaps that's what I need—a hard session on a squash court to knock some sense into me. Damn it, Ryan, I nearly ended up married there! What a fate!'

Ryan's smile didn't reach his eyes. Zach had a feeling that his didn't, either, but he didn't really care any more. He drained the malt, Ryan replenished the glass and they kicked the conversation around a little more until Zach decided that he'd had a narrow escape and marriage to Jill would have been a seriously major mistake.

Then Ryan put him to bed, and in the morning he woke up with a tongue three inches thick and stuck to the roof of his mouth, and pins and needles in both feet because

Scud was lying on his legs, and a gap beside him where Jill should have been, and he knew what Ryan had meant about being lonely.

Jill wasn't sure how to face Zach the next day. In fact, she didn't have to because he was in Theatre again for the morning and in a clinic for the afternoon, and his SHO did the ward rounds and checked the post-ops for him, except for the one Jill was specialling—who Robert Ryder checked.

He was a young man who had had an amputation that morning for a bone tumour, and Jill thought that paying attention to his needs might take her mind off her own misery.

She was wrong. In practice, he slept all day, heavily sedated, and she had nothing to take her mind off Zach except the need to check the instruments every now and again.

It was nothing like enough, and as a form of therapy it had to be classed as a resounding failure. She was glad at the end of the day when her replacement came and relieved her and she could go home.

Not yet, though. Mary had been giving her funny looks all day and, finally, just before she was due to go off duty, she called her into her room and shut the door.

'OK, what's going on?' she asked.

'Nothing,' Jill told her flatly.

'Rubbish. And don't tell me it's none of my business. When one of my staff looks like the world's coming to an end, that makes it my business.'

Jill chewed her lip and stared out of the window and said nothing.

'Zach?' Mary probed, more kindly.

'We've split up.'

Mary tsked and got her compassionate look on and Jill tried not to look at her in case she broke down. 'Poor love,' Mary was saying. 'How rotten for you. Did he tell you last night?'

'No,' Jill said shortly. 'I told him.'

Mary looked stunned. 'You—oh. He was in here earlier looking like death warmed up and I thought something must be wrong. Do you want to talk about it, my love?'

'No,' Jill said, a little harshly, and then felt guilty because the older woman was only being kind. 'No,' she said again, but more softly. 'I'm sorry, Mary, it's all too fresh.'

'That's all right, sweetheart, I understand.'

Sweetheart.

Jill swallowed and grabbed the doorhandle. 'I'm off now,' she told her superior. 'I'll see you at twelve tomorrow—I'm on a late.'

And she ran home, gulping down tears, and fell apart in the privacy of her bedroom. Then she got up, changed her clothes and cleaned the flat from top to bottom.

Not that it was dirty, exactly. She'd done the same the night before.

Oh, well, cleanliness was next to godliness and all that, and the activity helped keep her just marginally sane. Just so long as she could keep away from Zach, she'd be able to cope.

Her luck ran out the following afternoon. He came round to look at Duncan Buckley, the man who had had his leg amputated at mid-thigh in an attempt to halt the spread of his bone cancer. She was specialling him again, to give continuity of care, and Zach—as Robert Ryder's registrar—was responsible for his follow-up.

Before he examined the man he nodded to Jill and she nodded back, and that was it.

Simple—or so she thought.

He checked the charts, examined the monitors, looked at the aspirate from the wound drain, checked the stump and chatted to the man. Then he turned to Jill.

'Could I have a word?'

'Is it necessary?' she asked quietly.

One eyebrow quirked. 'Are you questioning my clinical judgement?'

She flushed scarlet. 'Sorry,' she mumbled. 'I didn't know what you wanted.'

Not me, she thought, and resisted the urge to ask him how his wedding plans were coming on. No. She wouldn't stoop to such indignities. Head high, she followed him out of the room and into the sister's office.

'Yes?' she said quietly.

'We've got the report from Pathology on his leg. It's not good. It seems it's a particularly aggressive form of cancer and his chances, frankly, are lousy. I thought you ought to be forewarned.'

'Oh. Will you tell him? He knows he's got cancer and he's pretty clued up, from what I can gather.'

Zach shrugged slightly. 'I don't know. I'll discuss it with Robert. I think he'll have to tell him if anyone's going to. If he asks, pretend you don't know and report to me or Robert—and for God's sake keep that girl away from him.'

'Angela?'

'Is that her? The one who spilled the beans to Gilroy. Keep her right away. He's got enough to contend with.'

'She's moved on, anyway.'

'Good. God help the next ward.' He hesitated at the door and let his professional façade slip for a moment.

'We're going to have to work together, Jill. Is it going to be a problem for you?'

She forced her chin up. 'Not if it isn't for you,' she lied.

His smile was strained. 'Good. That's all right, then,' he said, and he went out.

She wanted to scream, No, it's not all right! It's not all right at all!, but she couldn't. The show must go on, and all that junk.

She went back to the doomed Duncan Buckley and concentrated on making his time in her charge as good as it could be. It was the least she could do for him, after all, and little enough.

When she had a moment she also popped out to see Debbie Wright, the girl who had had a failed knee replacement removed. She was making good progress post-operatively, and was optimistic that her antibiotic therapy would be effective and that she would have another knee joint fitted in time. In the meantime, of course, she was unable to walk and would, for a while at least, be very dependent on others for her mobility.

She was able to sit out in a wheelchair now and her mother took her out into the garden for a little stroll round during the afternoon. They met up with Dolly Birkett in her wheelchair and came back together, pausing in the doorway of Duncan's room for a brief chat with Jill.

She was pleased to see Dolly mixing with the other patients. She had worried that the woman might find it hard after such a traumatic bereavement but she seemed remarkably cheerful, considering that her heel refused to mend and she was to be transferred to a specialist centre for implantation of an electrical stimulator to try and encourage the growth of new bone to bridge the gap where it had fractured and been packed with a bone graft.

She was due to leave the following day, and Jill thought

it was, perhaps, just as well. The woman did tend to regard her as her personal property, and with the situation as it was it could be difficult.

She thought she'd got away with it but the following morning, before her transport arrived, Dolly called Jill over and pressed something into her hand.

'Something I won in a magazine competition. It's nothing much, but I won't be able to enjoy it with my leg and all. It's for you and that nice boy you're so keen on,' she said. 'He's such a lovely person; I really hope you'll be happy together. At least you know he won't treat you like my Brian treated me.'

Jill looked at the slim envelope in her hand. 'Thank you, Dolly,' she murmured, unable to tell her that she and Zach were no longer an item. 'You shouldn't have done this.'

She waved a hand at Jill. 'Nonsense. You were wonderful to me, and he nearly killed you. Anyway, it didn't cost me a cent. You just enjoy yourselves.'

Jill was too busy being touched and trying to hide her feelings about Zach to exhibit any curiosity. She slipped the envelope into her pocket, sent Dolly on her way to London and went back to Duncan's room.

He was much more alert now, and Jill knew that he was about to start asking awkward questions. What she wasn't prepared for was the fact that he would also answer them.

'I'm dying, aren't I?' was the first remark.

'Not if we have anything to do with it,' Jill said firmly.

He fixed her with his steel-grey eyes and smiled. 'Don't patronise me, Sister. I know I'm dying. It's not really a question. The only question is when, and I guess the answer to that is quite soon.'

Jill didn't know how to respond to that at all. 'I think

you're jumping to conclusions,' she said quietly, after a long pause. 'I'm not qualified to answer your questions, and I'm not privy to enough information to be able to do it adequately. All I know is that the doctors haven't written you off yet, and I don't think you should.'

His smile was wry. 'I'm just facing facts. I'm thirty-two; I've had a great life so far; I've enjoyed every minute of it. If it's over now, I've got no regrets. At least I've had a hell of a lot of fun. If you want to feel sorry for someone, feel sorry for my mother and my girlfriend. They're the ones who'll suffer the most. I'll be out of it.'

She carried his words home with her that night, and it helped her put her own sorrow in perspective.

So she had made another error of judgement and allowed herself to trust Zach. She had been foolish, but she would get over it. She would survive, however painful the separation, and she would move on, and in time might even be able to think of him with fondness instead of anguish and disappointment.

For now, though, she preferred not to think of him at all because the wound was still too raw and the pain too intense.

She put her hand in her pocket to look for a tissue and her fingers closed around the envelope Dolly had given her that morning. It was creased now, and she pulled it out of her pocket and straightened it. What on earth could it be?

She opened the envelope carefully and pulled out a voucher for an all-expenses paid weekend for two in the honeymoon suite of a hotel in Cambridge. Strange how fortunes could change. Just a short time ago she would have been thrilled, and they would have had a wonderful time.

Now, just the thought of a honeymoon suite was enough to reduce her to tears.

Perhaps she should give it to him as a wedding present?

Zach was finding life without Jilly empty to the point of futility. He went to Cambridge for a training day and missed the point of what he was taught completely. He wasn't sleeping, he couldn't eat and on top of that—just to rub salt into the wound—he had to arrange his brother's wedding and keep him on the straight and narrow.

Dom wasn't being entirely co-operative, either.

'It's just a piece of paper,' he kept saying. 'Just a formality. Why do I have to marry her just to show commitment?'

'If it's just a formality, why not go through with it just to please Sarah?' Zach reasoned, meanwhile wishing that the woman he loved were half as keen to tie herself to him.

'It was fine until she got pregnant,' his brother grumbled.

'Babies are infinitely precious. You wait until you almost lose one, like Jody. That'll make you pay attention.'

'So she's been unlucky. She would have been better off without getting married.'

Zach thrust his hand through his hair in exasperation. 'So? She made a lousy choice. You've made an excellent one. The least you can do is back her up now in the one thing that really matters.'

Dom grumbled on for a few more minutes, but Zach knew that it was just a token protest. He'd be there for the wedding because basically he was a decent person and he loved Sarah. All Zach had to do was make sure it ran without a hitch.

He did what he could from home, but he had no choice but to phone the register office from the ward because of his working hours. He just hoped that Jill wouldn't come in so that he could concentrate on the call.

He was disappointed.

'We need to have another look at this rota. If Stella's going to change her holiday plans just because she's got a new boyfriend, we'll have to pray for stability for a while,' Mary said in desperation. 'Let's go in my office and do it.'

They went in and found Zach perched on the edge of the desk, talking down the phone.

'Right, so the wedding's booked for three-fifteen—Samuels. That's right. Yes, I'm Zachary Samuels. That's right. Fine. Thanks.'

Jill stood transfixed in the doorway. Oh, God, it was true. He *was* going to marry her. She dragged in a deep breath, turned and ran out of the room. Mary called after her, and then she heard footsteps following as she dashed into the kitchen.

The door wouldn't shut because there was a large, black-shod foot in the way and it rather messed up the shutability. She let go of the door and turned away, wrapping her arms round her chest and fighting for control of her wildly see-sawing heart.

The wedding. Oh, Lord, she didn't want to think about Zach's wedding—

There was a warm, gentle hand on her shoulder. 'Jilly?'

She shrugged his hand away. 'Did you have to do that here—at work?' she asked savagely.

'Do what?' he asked. His voice was puzzled. How dense could he be?

'That phone call.'

'Oh, come on, Jill, everybody makes personal calls from time to time.'

'Not that personal! Most of us don't book our weddings—and especially not in front of another lover!'

She could feel his eyes boring into the back of her neck. 'What the hell are you talking about?' he said softly. 'What other lover?'

'Yours, of course,' she snapped. 'This is your wedding we're talking about, isn't it?'

There was a stunned silence for a moment. 'Well, no, actually,' he said at last, 'it's my brother's. His girlfriend's pregnant, and he doesn't have the urge to commit in quite the way she'd like. I'm going to have to frogmarch him up the aisle, so to speak. I'm just making sure it gets done. Jill, why the hell should you think it was my wedding? You said you wouldn't marry me. Why would I be booking a wedding for myself?'

Jill turned slowly to face him. 'Your—brother?' she whispered. 'Pod's your *brother's* girlfriend?'

'Who the hell's Pod?' he demanded impatiently. 'Honestly, woman, you aren't making any sense at all. He's marrying a girl called Sarah Wakefield.'

'Tall, dark hair, pregnant?'

Zach frowned at her. 'Yes. How did you know? Has she been here asking for me? Is that what's wrong?'

Jill felt sick—sick and also faintly, dimly hopeful. 'No,' she told him slowly. 'She was at your house.'

He pulled his brows together hard. 'Sarah? Only once recently. You didn't meet her.'

'No—no, I didn't, but I saw her. You said she was beautiful, and you kissed her and told her you'd have to make sure she wasn't an unmarried mother—'

Puzzlement faded, replaced by understanding and an ice-cold, terrifying rage.

'You saw that and you concluded—what? Let me guess—that she was an old girlfriend come back to claim me? That the wedding was ours—hers and mine—and that I thought she was beautiful and desirable and you couldn't compete?'

He grabbed her and yanked her up against his chest. 'You saw us and you jumped to all sorts of conclusions, and then the next day you came round and told me you didn't love me?'

She nodded and closed her eyes. 'Yes,' she whispered.

'Why the hell couldn't you trust me?' he snarled. 'You never have. Right from the beginning you've been looking for evidence to support your theories. Well, let me ask you something, Jill—did it make you feel better when you thought you'd proved yourself right?'

He all but threw her down, and she hit her hip on the worktop and gasped with pain. 'No,' she said brokenly, 'it didn't make me feel better. It made me feel ten times worse. I was coming to tell you I loved you—that I wanted to marry you. Then I found you planning a wedding with somebody else. What was I supposed to think?'

'You could have asked me,' he bit out. 'Either then or the next day, you could have discussed it with me and given me the benefit of the doubt, but, oh, no, that wouldn't fit with your theory, would it? Well, let me tell you what to do with your theory, shall I? You can roll it up and— oh, forget it. You aren't worth the effort.'

And he strode out, slamming the door behind him and leaving Jill trembling against the worktop, her foolish fears exposed for what they were—alone with the terrible, bitter knowledge of all she had thrown away.

'You doing anything for lunch?'

Ryan looked up from his paperwork and shook his head. 'No. I was just finishing this then I was going to the canteen. Why?'

'Let's go over the road to the pub.'

Ryan didn't argue. He signed the sheet, stacked the papers and capped his pen, then stood up, hung his white coat on the back of the door and gestured to the door. 'Let's go.'

They went, and found a quiet spot on the grass in the pub's crowded garden, and while Zach stabbed prawns with his fork Ryan watched him and ate his salad and waited.

Finally Zach spoke.

'She thought Sarah was my girlfriend.'

'Pardon me? Sarah?'

Zach sighed and rammed his hand through his hair. 'Sarah—my brother Dom's girlfriend. She's pregnant. She was round stressing out about Dom not wanting to get married and her not feeling attractive and so on, and I was just hugging her and telling her she's lovely and we'd have to get her married and Jill must have come round and heard it.'

'And jumped to conclusions.'

'Yes. Ridiculous, isn't it?'

Ryan shook his head. 'No. It's a little garbled, but I think I get the picture. Jill arrives unannounced and finds you in a clinch with a pregnant girl, telling her she's beautiful and you'll have to see to it that she gets married, and she quite logically thinks you're going to marry the girl. Seems sensible to me. What else was she supposed to think?'

Zach stared at him as if he'd grown horns. 'But it's crazy! I'd only just proposed to her the night before—'

'So maybe she thought you couldn't possibly mean it. Maybe she thought you were on the rebound from this girl, or that you just wanted to get married and anyone would do, or whatever. Any one of a dozen things would have been quite reasonable under the circumstances.'

Zach felt stunned. Was it true? Did Jill really have a good reason to think that he was going to marry Sarah?

And, if so, how understandable her response.

'Ah, hell, Ryan—so what do I do now?'

'Find out if she does love you?'

He snorted. 'What, and spend the rest of my life afraid to speak to another woman in case she misunderstands?'

Ryan speared one of Zach's neglected prawns and chewed it thoughtfully. 'Maybe you should get this trust business sorted out between you once and for all. It seems to me that she's overly suspicious but you do seem to expect her to understand any damn thing you do without suspicion, and I think that's a bit much. You have to allow her the natural feelings of possessiveness that will keep her monogamous. Just think—if she didn't care what you did and with whom, would you be able to trust her?'

It was a very good point, and one which Zach had overlooked.

'No,' he said heavily. 'No, of course not. But I still can't cope with her doubting me every time she hears me laugh.'

'No, of course not. I think, as I say, you've got to get that sorted out before you can move on. Do you want those prawns?'

'Yes. Get your own.' Zach speared three and ate them, then pushed the plate towards Ryan. 'Have some, then.'

His friend grinned. 'I think I'll do that. And go and see her after work and sort this out—before you both go round the bend.'

Jill struggled through the rest of that shift, mechanically performing tasks that were simple and that even she couldn't manage to foul up. All the time her mind was reeling with the knowledge that he wasn't getting married at all. She swung wildly between hope and despair because he had been so hard just before he'd slammed out of the kitchen. For the most part despair got the upper hand, and she was almost useless at work.

Then Mary sent her home, and she went back to her flat to find Zach sitting outside on the garden wall, waiting.

She turned on her heel and started to walk away but he came after her, catching her up in a few short strides and stopping her with a gentle but firm hand on her arm.

'Jilly, we need to talk,' he said quietly.

'Is there anything to say?'

He sighed shortly. 'Yes—but not here in the street with your neighbours hanging out of the windows and listening to every word.'

'I don't think I could shock them any more,' she said frankly. 'They've got used to my strange behaviour in the past few weeks.'

She turned anyway and went back to her flat, letting them in and walking down the hall to the kitchen. She ran the cold tap, filled a glass and drained it then set the glass down.

'You wanted to talk to me,' she said flatly.

'Yes. Can we sit down?'

'Will it take that long?'

He sighed. 'Suit yourself.'

She forced herself to meet his eyes, and noticed for the first time the lines of strain around them. He wasn't coping at all well with this, no better than her, and why should he? He'd said he loved her. It was probably true, and her stupid jealousy had destroyed both their lives. She owed him at least the benefit of listening to what he had to say.

'I'm sorry. Come in the sitting room.'

She led him in and they sat on separate chairs, both

avoiding the sofa where they had made love on several occasions.

He stared at his hands for a while, then looked up at her and his eyes were desolate. 'I don't know if there's any hope for us,' he began, 'but if there is, something's got to give. I know that my feelings for you won't change; that I love you and probably always will. I know I would never willingly hurt you, and that without you my life's empty and meaningless.

'I also know that I can't live my life under a cloud of suspicion and mistrust. OK, this incident is clearly a gross misunderstanding, but if you'd trusted me—if you'd wanted me enough to fight for me—you would have walked right in and challenged Sarah. You would have said, "He's mine, you can't have him," and you would have tossed her out on her ear. But you didn't, did you? You preferred to believe the worst of me, and I guess you always will.'

He looked down at his hands again, while Jill bit her lip and considered his words and realised the truth of what he was saying.

'I'm sorry,' she said numbly, her throat clogged with tears. 'I want to trust you. I want to believe in you, but every man I trust lets me down. I just expect it now. Zach, I'm not sure I'm capable of trusting you—or anyone. I'm just too insecure.'

'It works both ways, Jilly,' he said softly. 'I have to be able to trust you not to jump to conclusions and go off half-cocked every time you catch me on the phone to my mother, for instance. I have to be able to trust you to stand by me and be there for me when things go wrong—if a female patient accuses me of indecent assault, for instance. It happens, you know. Could you stand up for me and say that I wouldn't have done it? Or would you be more inclined to say, "I knew it. He always had it in him."?'

She stared at him, searching his eyes and wondering how she would feel. Was he right?

Probably.

Oh, Lord, was she really so shallow and untrusting that she couldn't have faith in him?

She looked away, her heart breaking. She was going to lose him because she couldn't trust him, and he had done nothing—nothing—to make her doubt him.

He stood up and walked over to her, drawing her to her feet. 'I still love you, Jilly,' he murmured. 'I still want to marry you, but it's up to you. When you can come to me and say you trust me, and you'll fight for me, and you're going to make damn sure I never look at another woman because I just won't ever want to, then we'll try again. Until then, sweetheart, the ball's in your court.'

And he bent and kissed her lightly but lovingly on her mouth, then turned and left the room.

She stood there for an age, wondering how she could be so stupid as to jeopardise her life with him because of her foolish insecurity. And then she remembered the look on the face of the wife of her nemesis, the man who had started all this fear. Disappointment, yes, but not surprise. She was past being surprised by him and his women. She had almost looked sorry for Jill, in fact.

How terrible to be tied to someone like that, but had she known at the outset that he was the unfaithful type? Jill didn't think so. Why would she have married him?

To change him? She should have had Mary O'Brien there to tell her that it didn't work. She hadn't changed Zach. He still laughed and chatted and socialised with everyone at every opportunity. Did she just resent his easy camaraderie?

Whatever, she longed for some of it now—for his warm

and funny humour and his arms around her and his gentle teasing. Heavens, how she missed him!

She sniffed and blinked. Silly, to cry now. She had hope now. He wasn't marrying Pod, and he still wanted her. As he'd said, the ball was in her court.

Would she drop it?

CHAPTER TEN

JILL's first challenge came the following morning on the ward. Zach was looking at Debbie Wright's leg, and she was telling him how she'd modelled tights for one of the big manufacturers before her accident.

He looked at the other leg, grinned and told her that it would be a shame to deprive everyone and she'd have to model stockings.

Jill was shocked and horrified, but Debbie laughed until the tears ran down her face. Zach patted her shoulder and moved on, unaware of Jill's reaction.

Or so she thought. He hung back and waited for her as they moved on to the next patient on his rounds, and he looked her in the eye and said, 'What?'

'You don't think it was a bit familiar?' she said.

'No, little prude, I don't. She's feeling very insecure about her looks; she's trying her best to be brave and philosophical, and she brought the subject up, after all. I just made a joke of it to cheer her up. Is that so wrong? Or are you jealous?'

She felt silly then. 'No, of course not,' she lied, and he smiled understandingly.

'Trust me, sweetheart. I don't have fantasies about her legs wrapped around my waist.'

Jill flushed scarlet, but Zach just smiled knowingly and moved on.

The next day he was chatting up another doctor—or so it appeared. Damn him, she thought, but when she had to go over to the workstation she overheard the girl saying,

'Of course we could always go together—save petrol and make the journey more fun. We could maybe stop off on the way home—'

Jill gave her a chilling look and turned to Zach. 'Would you pick some bread up on the way home tonight, please, darling?' she said sweetly, and left the pair of them to sort it out between themselves.

He found her a few minutes later. 'Was that an invitation or a shot across her bows?'

Jill gave him a level look. 'What do you think?'

'I could have got rid of her myself, you know—or didn't you trust me to do that?'

She met his eyes and found approval lurking in their cobalt depths. 'I wasn't taking chances,' she said flatly. 'Anyway, she's a man-eater.'

'Mmm,' he said thoughtfully, but his eyes were twinkling. 'Listen, about this wedding.'

Even the word sent a chill through her. 'What about it?'

'I've told my parents that you're coming with me. I don't know how you feel about it, but I'd appreciate it if you'd come. I've told them about you, and I don't want to ruin the wedding by telling them that it's all off so soon before.'

'When is it?' she asked, wondering why her presence or absence would make any difference.

'Saturday.'

'This Saturday? I think I'm on duty.'

'Mary's changed it.'

Jill stared at him. 'Why?'

'Because I asked her to.'

'Wasn't that a bit presumptuous?' she said stiffly.

'Oh, Jilly, for heaven's sake don't get stuffy on me. I want you to come. I asked Mary if you'd be able to and she said she could easily change the rota. Her husband's playing golf so she'll swap with you. It was as simple and as complicated as that. No great devious dealings.'

His voice was tinged with impatience, and Jill realised that she'd overreacted yet again. Still, she didn't like having her life dictated to her. 'I'll think about coming,' she said, 'but if this relationship's going to work, it's going to have to work both ways. I won't watch your every move if you don't dictate mine. OK?'

He looked surprised, as if it had never occurred to him that she might object to him changing the rota.

'I suppose you didn't think that I might have had other plans and was working on Saturday to keep another day free? I do have a life that doesn't include you.'

Too much of it, far too much at the moment, and there had been no other plans—but it wouldn't hurt him to think she was busy.

He apologised, and she immediately felt a heel. 'I didn't, as it happens, but please don't do it again without asking.'

'I won't.'

He looked thoughtful. Good. Just so long as she wasn't the only one having to reassess her attitude. . .

The next few days were busy, as usual, but she still seemed to see him all the time. Was it deliberate policy? she wondered. And every time she saw him he was at the centre of a laughing crowd.

Sometimes he would look up and meet her eye challengingly, and she would force herself to smile and carry on. She found it easier to busy herself with work, and she found Duncan Buckley taking a lot of her time.

He was up and about now for an hour at a time, down in the physiotherapy department having walking lessons with the inflatable PPAM or pneumatic post-amputation mobility aid. He was also being encouraged to sit out in a chair, but he had to spend a large part of every day or night lying on his front to prevent contractures in his leg. Without the weight of his lower leg to anchor it, the strong muscles used for pulling the leg forward in walking would tighten up and pull the stump up.

That could make it difficult or impossible to walk with an artificial limb, but whenever she mentioned it to him and told him to roll onto his front he did so only to be obliging and not because he believed that he would ever need an artificial leg.

'I won't be alive; what does it matter?' he said mildly to the physio on one occasion, and the poor girl was very upset.

'He's so nice,' she said to Jill. 'Is it really so certain that he'll die?'

Jill nodded. They'd had the results of his latest scan, and there were metastases or secondaries in his other leg, his hip and his shoulder. So far they were symptomless, but nevertheless they were there and there was no possibility of further surgery.

'He won't even have chemotherapy and radiotherapy, he says, and he only had the first leg off because his family were so insistent that he should try everything. He always said there was no point and, of course, he was right.'

'Poor man.'

Jill smiled. 'Not according to him. He's had a great life, he says, and he has no regrets.'

That changed, though—dramatically—in the next few hours because his girlfriend came in to tell him that she had just discovered she was pregnant.

Suddenly he had something to live for—a child that he wouldn't live to see unless he underwent the treatment the oncologist advised. Jill found him in tears just before the end of her shift, and she sat on the edge of his bed, put her arms round him and held him while he cried.

'I didn't think I'd care about dying,' he said wretchedly, 'but now, suddenly, it matters like hell. I don't want to die yet. I want to live, and see my child, and I don't want to die—'

She hugged him again, handed him tissues and let him talk about the baby and when it was due and how he felt, and how his girlfriend felt, and how he wanted the treatment—any treatment—that would prolong his life just enough so that he could see the baby.

She promised to talk to the doctors and get them to come and see him, and when she stood up she found Zach watching her through the open door. She went over to him.

'That looked cosy,' he said, and he sounded a little short. She blinked and looked at him closely.

'You're jealous,' she stated.

'Petty, isn't it?'

'Oh, very, but it hurts like hell, doesn't it?'

Understanding dawned in his eyes. 'So what was it all about?'

She sighed and rubbed her hands over her face. 'His girlfriend's pregnant. He wants treatment.'

'It won't work,' Zach said quietly.

'I know. He does, too, but he wants to live to see the baby.'

'I'll ring the oncologist. Have you thought any more about the weekend?'

'The wedding?' She nodded. 'Yes, I'll come. I'd like to meet your family.'

'Good. I'll ring the oncologist and drop in later to make the arrangements with you, OK?'

'OK. Go and talk to him.'

'Will do.'

She left him and went home, and found a cat curled up on her bench. She mixed some mineral water and fresh orange juice and took it out in the garden, sat beside the cat and thought about Duncan.

She'd always felt that he was too philosophical, both about dying and about the amputation, but perhaps that was because—despite his protestations of happiness—he didn't have anything he'd mind leaving behind.

She thought of dying as an alternative to spending all those years with Zach, and realised she would go to any lengths, take any treatments, rather than be cheated of one minute of his company.

So why, then, was she being so silly about telling him so? She should just say that she'd decided to trust him, and if he ever proved her wrong she'd kill him with her bare hands. Then they could get on with the business of loving each other.

Yes. She'd tell him, but not yet. After the wedding.

Her decision made, she thought that Saturday would never come. The next day dawned bright and sunny and with no warning of the spate of illness amongst the staff. Jill, ever sceptical, wondered how many of them just felt the need to spend some time in the sunshine and were skiving.

Not that she had long to debate the problem. She was busy with a theatre list, giving the pre-meds and last reassurances, calling the anaesthetist to pull someone off the list at the last minute because she'd developed a chesty cough overnight—it was continuous, relentless, and she found that some of the staff became even more inadequate under pressure.

That did nothing for her temper, and she had to wrestle with her self-control and not bite their heads off.

Then they had an emergency admission, a young woman

with severe spinal injuries. She had suffered a serious whiplash injury to the thoracic spine, following a sharp blow just below her shoulder-blades, and all functions below her chest were compromised.

She had fallen off a horse and landed across a log and, although she had seemed all right at first, by the time she was admitted to the ward she was starting to complain of loss of sensation. Within half an hour she had lost control of bowel and bladder, her legs were paralysed and her blood pressure had crashed.

'She's got spinal shock,' Jill said to the staff nurse with her. 'Call Zach.'

She bent over the girl. 'Anna? Anna, can you hear me? I'd going to put an oxygen mask on you to help you breathe, and I'm going to raise your legs and arms. OK?'

She picked up a lightweight chair, turned it over and put a pillow over it. She carefully lifted Anna's legs onto it, then she fixed the oxygen mask, put the girl's hands on her stomach and sent the staff nurse back to fetch a trolley laid up for IV infusion.

Zach was there moments later, setting up the drip and running it in fast to increase her circulating blood volume. 'Has she haemorrhaged?'

'Not as far as I know,' Jill reported. 'I think it looks like spinal shock—she's lost function and sensation below the chest, and the injury's at T6.'

'OK.' He checked her quickly, asked for a cardiac monitor to be set up and then once her blood volume had increased he turned to Jill. 'She looks better. I don't think we need to set up an arterial pressure monitor. Have we got scans and X-rays?'

'Scans are booked for any minute now. X-rays are here.'

He snapped them up onto the light-box, studied them in silence and shook his head. 'No sign of fracture or dislocation, just swelling. We'll need the results of the scan to see if there's any significant soft tissue damage, but I don't want her moved for a little while. I want to be happy she's stable and not going deeper into shock before we start running round the hospital with her, and when she does go down I want you with her.'

'Today, of all days,' Jill sighed.

'Staffing problems?'

'You could say that. Oh, well, the ward will have to run itself. I've got a qualified member of staff on duty. She'll have to cope.'

The ward did run itself but only because one of the people who had rung in sick felt 'better' and arrived at lunchtime, looking very relaxed and happy.

Jill soon got her working, and as soon as Zach was happy about Anna she took her down to the radiology department for her scan, and waited with her.

The results were encouraging and confirmed the diagnosis of spinal shock, which relieved Anna's parents who had been convinced that she would be paralysed for life.

'It may last hours, days or even weeks,' Zach warned them. 'We have no way of knowing, but what we can tell you is that she should recover completely without loss of function. I'll get a neurologist to discuss it with you further, but orthopaedically we're happy she's got no permanent damage or anything that will lead to permanent damage. The only problem she may have is a weak area in that part of her spine, and she may need an operation to repair or tighten ligaments in the future.'

Anna was understandably relieved, and feeling better now that her blood pressure had risen a little. Her parents sat with her and she dozed off, and after that everything settled down and went back to the normal chaotic routine.

Predictably, because they had staffing problems, Jill was

too busy to slip out to the shops and look for a wedding outfit to wear. It needed to be special, she thought, and that night she pulled *that* dress out of the back of her wardrobe. She had rescued it from the bin, sure that she would never wear it again and yet unable to throw it out, for some sentimental reason.

She had it dry-cleaned at the cleaners round the corner, and was amazed at how good it looked. So she was a stick insect. So what? At least she'd look a well-dressed stick insect in it. And, if she remembered rightly, that jacket she had bought last year was just the right length to go with it and dress it up a bit.

Co-incidentally she could hide under it, of course...

The wedding was noisy, exuberant and right up Zach's street. His whole family were like him—warm, loving, extrovert—it was easy to see where he'd got it from.

His brother, especially, was very like him, and he was clearly smitten with Pod. She looked radiant, pregnant and proud of it, her glowing skin and bright eyes testament to her health and happiness.

It was going to be difficult to remember to call her Sarah. She'd got used to thinking of her as Pod. Maybe when the pod had ripened and she wasn't pregnant any more it would be easier.

Jill circulated with Zach, being introduced to countless members of his large and extended family. They were all talking a mile a minute, and she felt left out, but she kept the smile on her face and stayed beside him.

It was hard not to. She was anchored to his side for the most part by a powerful and possessive arm, but at one juncture she managed to slip away and was standing in the shade of a tree in his parents' garden where the impromptu reception was being held and watching him.

A brunette came up to him, slipped her arms round his neck and pressed her body up against him. Jill felt insecurity and anger sweep through her, just as she heard a quiet voice behind her say, 'She always did have a soft spot for him. That's his cousin, Mel. She's a model. No brains but a beautiful body. Unfortunately she's too stupid to understand that he wants more than that from a woman.'

Jill turned and met Zach's mother's eyes. 'He's always surrounded by women.'

She laughed softly. 'He always has been. Even at nursery school all his friends were girls. They used to fight over him and carry his bag.'

Jill gave a disbelieving chuckle. 'At four?'

'Oh, yes. He's always had terrible trouble fending girls off. It's those eyes, and he's so friendly, too, and open with everybody. They all just get the wrong end of the stick, and he's too kind to tell them to go to hell.'

Jill remembered him telling her that he wouldn't want her unless she was prepared to fight for him. So be it. She was about to march across the lawn when she saw Zach ease the girl away from his body, kiss her lightly on the cheek and release her.

He came towards her, unaware of how close he'd come to being the subject of a brawl. 'There you are. You disappeared.'

He put an arm round her shoulders, grinned at his mother and gestured at the crowd. 'Good do. Everybody's having fun.'

'Yes, I think they are. I owe you one. I never thought I'd get Dominic up the aisle, even after Sarah became pregnant.'

'Ah,' Zach said with a laugh, 'you should have asked me earlier.'

'Why should I assume you'd help me marry him off?'

she asked drily. 'You've never shown any inclination to the state of matrimony yourself.'

Zach looked at Jill, and behind the smile she could see the doubt and hesitation. 'Perhaps because I've never before thought I wanted to get married.'

His mother looked from one to the other and back again. 'So that's the way the land lies?' she murmured. 'Well, keep me posted. We've had some practice now at weddings. We should be able to manage one even quicker, if necessary.'

She moved away, leaving them alone, and Jill tipped her head back and met his eyes. 'Why did you tell her that?'

'Because it's the truth. I've never kept anything from my mother. I didn't say I'd asked you or you'd agreed.'

Jill scanned the crowd. Mel was still in evidence. 'Your cousin would be disappointed if I snapped you up,' she said.

'Mel?' His eyes followed hers. 'She's harmless. She's too feather-brained to be anything else.'

Just then someone called him over, and he excused himself and went and joined them. A bachelor crowd, she thought, and scanned the crowd for Mel again. Perhaps a little word?

She crossed the lawn and smiled at the girl, and received a lovely smile in return. Good grief, she was stunning that close up. Her skin was like translucent silk. It would look awful with scratches all over it. Jill stuffed her hands in the pockets of her jacket.

'I'm Jill,' she said calmly. 'Jill Craig. And you're Mel.'

'That's right. You're with Zach, aren't you?'

Jill nodded. 'That's right. Did Zach happen to mention we're getting married?'

Her eyes widened like pretty, black-lashed saucers. 'Married?' she mouthed. 'Zach? Good grief. Well, it had to happen sooner or later. I would have liked him to marry me, but he thinks I'm just a feather-brain. He's right, of course,' she said, and Jill felt that there was a great deal of shrewd logic behind the dumb façade.

'What was that about?' Zach murmured, arching one eyebrow and rejoining her.

She slipped her arm through his.

'Just a chat,' she said blithely.

He eyed Mel's departing back. 'What did you say to her?'

'Nothing much,' she lied.

'Warning her off?'

'Whatever gave you that idea?'

He stared at her for a long moment, then his mouth creased in a slow smile, a deep laugh rumbled up from his chest and he put his arms round her and swung her round and round in the air.

'Oh, Jill,' he murmured, finally setting her on her feet. 'I think we might be getting somewhere.'

She disentangled herself from his arms and straightened her jacket. 'I haven't met your sister yet,' she told him.

'Which one?'

'Jody. The one with Scud and the baby.'

'She's not here—she rang to say the baby had a bit of a cold and she daren't leave him or make him come all the way up here.'

'Up here' was near Peterborough, not far from where she was but too far for the baby in the heat—especially after the tricky start he had had.

'You'll meet her. She's going to have Scud back soon and see how she gets on with him. He loves it with me, but it's not fair with me being out all day and having to leave him shut in.'

'Where is he today?' Jill asked.

'With Ryan. That'll strain our friendship,' Zach said with a chuckle.

Just then somebody banged something to attract everyone's attention, and Zach's father announced that Sarah and Dom were about to leave. They all went out and threw confetti and wished them luck and then, after they had driven away, the guests started to thin out.

'Time to go,' Zach said. 'You're on duty early tomorrow, and I have got so much to do on the barn you wouldn't believe it. Anyway, I ought to collect Scud off Ryan before he totally destroys their house. He's a good friend and I don't want to take advantage.'

Jill was sorry they were leaving. She liked his family, and she sensed that they liked her. She hoped so. They were going to be stuck with each other for a long while!

CHAPTER ELEVEN

BY THE time they got back and collected Scud it was late, so Zach dropped Jill off at her flat. He escorted her to the door, and as she turned to say goodbye he caught her shoulders in his hands and drew her closer.

'Thank you for coming with me today,' he murmured.

She smiled, the first genuine smile she'd given him for days. 'I enjoyed it. Your family are lovely.'

He grinned. 'Thanks. Sarah thinks so, too. Her parents are both dead and she's only got one sister, much older. She found us a bit much at first.'

'I can see why,' Jill said wryly. 'All of you together can be quite intimidating.'

'Were you intimidated?'

She thought about it for a moment. 'No, I don't think so. I was a bit, for a few minutes, but you're all the same. It was like being in a room full of Zachs.'

'Is that good or bad?'

She pursed her lips and cocked her head on one side and pretended to think about it, but she couldn't keep the smile down for long. 'I think it has to be good,' she said softly.

He stared into her eyes for an endless moment, then he smiled slowly. 'Good,' he said in quiet satisfaction. 'And now I'm going to go before I give in to my instincts and take you to bed.'

'You don't have to go,' she protested softly.

'Yes I do,' he corrected, tapping her lightly on the nose,

'because you've got to do some serious thinking before we go any further.'

I've done it, she could have said, but she was on duty and he had to work on the barn and she wanted to be able to savour holding him again after all this time.

So she stood up on tiptoe and kissed his cheek, and let him go.

It was the last time, she swore—the very last.

She was on duty early the next morning and, of course, there was the usual mixture of old patients who were making steady recoveries and the new emergency patients who had come in overnight.

At least, she thought, they didn't have to deal with the routine operation list as well!

Duncan Buckley was due to start his cancer therapy that week, and she sensed that he still needed a great deal of support. Physically, though, his wound was healing well and he was making excellent progress with the walking aid, according to the physio.

Perhaps once he got his artificial leg and was more mobile and his treatment was under way he would feel a little more positive.

She was too busy to spend much time with him, though, because of the new admissions. Amongst them, they had three members of one family on the ward, the result of a car crash on the way home from a wedding.

Too much to drink? Quite likely, Jill thought, and remembered that Zach had drunk only one glass of champagne because he was driving, and he had left half of that.

She checked the man's traction on his broken femur, rearranged the sling suspending his arm so that it wasn't digging into the back of his upper arm, and assured him that the mass of black stitches in his wife's eyebrow would leave hardly a mark. Clearly his conscience was playing up.

His wife, apart from the cut on her forehead and a mass of cuts and bruises, had a broken wrist and a crack in one of the metatarsal bones in her foot. She would be able to go home later.

Their daughter, seventeen and very conscious of her swollen nose and eye, lurked miserably in the bed and refused to be cheered up. She had dislocated her hip and was in traction, like her father, and was not at all happy. 'It hurts,' she wailed, 'and I look awful, and my boy-friend's going to come in and see me and he'll go right off me—'

'In which case he's not worth having,' Jill told her bluntly. 'You're lucky not to be more seriously injured, and if he was a decent human being he'd be worried about you.'

Nothing gets through to the vulnerable child behind the vain adolescent, Jill thought later. No comfort could be offered that would make her feel better—at least not by someone detached, as she was. Perhaps the boy-friend?

He was a star. He told her that she looked very colourful, kissed her on her undamaged side and gave her flowers and chocolates, sitting by her holding her hand and staring into her one open eye and obviously saying outrageous things because the side of her face that wasn't bruised went a very pretty shade of pink.

Jill left them to it. She had plans of her own tonight that included flowers and chocolates and lots of eye con-tact, and she could hardly wait to go off duty and set her plans in motion. . .

*　　　*　　　*

Zach worked himself to death on the barn. It was reaching the stage where it looked almost like a home, and he wanted to finish the sitting-room, at least, so that he had somewhere to retreat to that wasn't building site.

Anyway, it stopped him thinking about Jill. He was see-sawing between wild optimism and extreme caution, and the strain was killing him.

By five o'clock he had just hung the last picture and stood back to admire his handiwork when his doorbell started barking. Dusting off his hands, he went to let his visitor in.

Jill put on a soft, floaty dress which buttoned through the front and was cool and pretty and not too dressed up. She thought of wearing the slinky tube she'd worn the previous day, but decided that one could have too much of a good thing and the last time she'd worn it to visit him at the barn had been a disaster.

She put the flowers and chocolates on the passenger seat of her car, strapped herself in and drove to Zach's. It was difficult. Her heart was in her mouth and it made life very uncomfortable and awkward.

Not as uncomfortable and awkward as finding a strange car parked beside his.

Damn. Oh, well, she wasn't going away now for anybody.

Scud came bounding up without barking, used to her by now and happy to see her.

He was disgustingly pleased with himself about something, she thought, and ruffled his ears lovingly. 'Hello, rascal,' she murmured. 'What have you been doing to make you so happy?'

He grinned and swiped his lolling tongue over her wrist. 'Thanks, mate,' she said drily, and wiped her hand on his coat. He waited while she picked up the flowers and chocolates, then trotted beside her to the door.

She drew a deep, steadying breath and went in.

There were voices in the sitting-room, and the smell of fresh paint mingled with the aroma of real coffee. She dumped the flowers in the sink, put the chocolates in the fridge and followed Scud through to the sitting-room.

Zach was sitting on the sofa, his arm round a lovely girl with dark hair and beautiful, clear skin. Her bust was falling out of her skimpy little top, her legs looked impossibly long and slender sticking out of elegant, tailored shorts and the strappy sandals on her feet showed off her beautifully manicured toenails to perfection.

Jill wished she'd worn the other dress.

Just then the woman leant her head against Zach's and sighed. 'It's so lovely to see you again,' she murmured. 'I've missed you.'

'Me, too.' He turned his head and pressed his lips to her hair, and his hand on her shoulder tightened in an affectionate squeeze.

Jill wasn't the only one who objected to that familiarity. Scud trotted up to Zach and nudged his hand, and he looked up, blinked and got to his feet.

'Jill! I didn't expect you till later.'

I'll bet, she thought. Did he look guilty? She didn't care. She was hopping mad and ready to tell him—and her on the sofa, eyeing Jill with frank curiosity.

She met the woman's gorgeous blue eyes unflinchingly.

'I don't believe we've met,' she said. 'I'm Jill—Zach's fiancée. I don't know who you are or what impression he might have given you, but he's taken.'

Zach made a strange noise—halfway between a cough and a chuckle—and the woman unfolded those hateful legs and stood up, smiling broadly.

'Thank God for that,' she said, in a voice that sounded very much like Zach's. She held out her hand. 'I'm his sister Jody.'

Jill caught her jaw just before it hit the deck. 'Oh,' she said weakly. Talk about having the wind taken out of your sails! 'Sorry. You just looked—well. Sorry.'

Zach put his arm round her and gave her a hug. 'Don't apologise to her. You can't have the slightest idea how long I've waited to hear you say something like that.'

She turned towards him and met his eyes, blazing with love and laughter, and dropped her head against his chest. 'I feel an idiot,' she mumbled.

The hug tightened. 'Did I ever mention how much I love you?' he said.

She tipped her head back. 'You did, but don't imagine that lets you off the hook for the future.'

He grinned. 'Yes, ma'am.' He turned to Jody. 'May I make a suggestion?'

'I'm on my way,' Jody said with a matching grin. 'Have fun, girls and boys. I'll try and make it to *your* wedding.'

'You do that,' Zach said warmly, and drew Jody into their hug. He kissed her forehead, patted her bottom and sent her off.

Scud stood at the door and watched her go, turned back to Jill and Zach and gazed at them despairingly. It was quite obvious that they weren't about to play with him.

He flopped down on the rug, dropped his head onto his paws and sighed. It was going to be a long, boring evening. . .

Jill woke to the sound of birds outside the window—and Zach's soft snores inside. She poked him in the ribs. 'Hey.'

He cracked an eye open. 'Hey, yourself. Whatever happened to "Good morning, darling"?' he grumbled.

She grinned. 'We're married now. Don't need all that stuff.'

He snagged her wrist and pulled her over him. 'Cheeky,' he murmured, and kissed her soundly. 'Good morning, darling.'

'Good morning, darling,' she parroted dutifully, and rolled onto her back, staring up at the canopy of the magnificent four-poster bed. 'Wasn't it kind of Dolly Birkett to give us her prize?' she said thoughtfully.

'Mmm—and so conveniently timed. Mind you, she was right, she didn't have a use for it, really. A honeymoon suite on your own after her recent history is a little superflous.'

'Perfect for us, though, and I reckon we earned it. I didn't enjoy being shot at.'

Zach shuddered and pulled her closer. 'Don't.'

She kissed him softly. 'All over now. Just wedded bliss into the hereafter—which is where you'll be if you make a habit of snoring.'

'I don't snore,' he protested.

'Of course not.' She rolled onto her back and stretched luxuriously. 'Your mother does a good line in weddings, doesn't she?'

Zach chuckled and stretched out beside her across the huge bed. 'It's all the practice. Still, that's it now. We're all married—except for Jody, and she doesn't want to get married again.'

'Maybe she'll meet someone she loves,' Jill said, absently trailing her fingers through the fine, soft curls scattered across his chest. She bent her head and flicked her tongue over one dusky copper nipple. It puckered and hardened to a tiny point. Satisfying. She turned to the other one. 'After all, I did.'

'Mmm,' Zach groaned softly. 'Maybe. Ah-h-h. . .'

She trailed the tip of her tongue down his chest and dipped it in his navel. He folded in half and squirmed away, laughing. 'That's just too ticklish,' he said.

'I like it,' she challenged.

'Do you now?'

He pushed her over onto her back and blew a raspberry on her tummy. She giggled and reached for him, threading her fingers through his hair and pulling him up until she could reach his mouth. Then she kissed him, and they forgot about laughing. They forgot about everything. It might have been weeks instead of hours since they had last celebrated their love.

They drifted back to earth slowly and Zach stood up, stretched and went over to the window. There was a magnificent view of the river, and he turned back to Jill.

'Nice morning. We should go for a walk.'

'No point. We haven't got the dog, and we don't need any more exercise!'

He chuckled, then came back and sat beside Jill. 'I hope Scud's all right back with Jody. He's got a bit used to having the freedom of the fields and the wood.' His hand absently cupped her breast with familiar affection. 'Actually, rather too much freedom. He's going to be a father, apparently. We've been promised one of the puppies, but I don't think we'll be able to take it. They need so much attention.'

Jill smiled serenely. 'Then it's just as well I'll be at home to look after it, isn't it?'

Zach's brow creased, and Jill smoothed out the skin. 'Don't frown,' she scolded lovingly. 'It takes a hundred and fifteen muscles to frown and only twelve to smile. I'd hate you to waste energy.'

He chuckled and caught her hand. 'Why will you be at home?' he asked deliberately.

She smiled again. 'With the baby.'

'Baby? What baby?'

'Our baby,' she said, as if it were so obvious. 'We were a little careless once or twice.'

'The night you came and told my sister to take a hike.' She grinned. 'Exactly.'

His face broke into a wide smile. 'A baby,' he said wonderingly, and then he gathered her lovingly into his arms.

'I might even get a bust,' she murmured.

'You've got a bust,' he protested, putting her away at arm's length and looking down at it. 'A very pretty one. I love it. I hope it doesn't get too big.'

'But you don't like stick insects. You said so to Sarah.'

He shook his head and tutted. 'Dominic doesn't like stick insects. I was telling Sarah what she needed to hear.'

'Well, damn,' she grumbled. 'You might have told me that. I was considering getting implants!'

He chuckled and hauled her up against his chest. 'Don't you dare. I love you, Mrs Samuels, just the way you are, and I always will.'

She laid her head on his shoulder and smiled.

That sounded wonderful.

**Look out next month for Ryan's own story,
THE PERFECT WIFE AND MOTHER?,
in the exciting sequel to Caroline Anderson's
Audley Memorial Duo.**

MILLS & BOON®

Medical Romance™

COMING NEXT MONTH

THE PERFECT WIFE AND MOTHER?
by Caroline Anderson
Audley Memorial Hospital

Ryan O'Connor wanted a lover. No commitment, no ties. And
Ginny Jeffries agreed, against her better judgement, to
accept Ryan O'Connor's terms. But being his lover meant
deepening ties with Ryan and his two small children, and all
she could see ahead was heartbreak...

INTIMATE PRESCRIPTION by Margaret Barker

Adam Lennox was surprised to see that Trisha Redman was a
mother. Eight years previously she had refused to marry him
because she was fearful of a physical relationship. So how
could she enjoy a physical relationship with another man?
Would Trisha tell Adam the truth?

PROMISE OF A MIRACLE by Marion Lennox
Gundowring Hospital

Meg Preston's quiet visit to Gundowring took an unexpected
turn when she fell into the path—and home—of Rob Daniels.
Before she knew it she was bound up in the Gundowring way
of life and was falling in love with Rob! But Meg had a fiancé
waiting in England...

WINNING THROUGH by Laura MacDonald

Dr Harry Brolin forecast that Kirstin Patterson would only
survive one month as a GP in his tough inner city practice.
She soon proved that she could handle even the most
perilous of situations. But could she handle her dangerous
feelings for Harry?

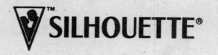

™ SILHOUETTE®

Tempting...Tantalising...Terrifying!

Strangers in the night

Three spooky love stories in one compelling volume by three masters of the genre:

Dark Journey by Anne Stuart
Catching Dreams by Chelsea Quinn Yarbro
Beyond Twilight by Maggie Shayne

Available: July 1997

Price: £4.99

SUMMER SEARCH

How would you like to win a year's supply of Mills & Boon® books? Well you can and they're FREE! Simply complete the competition below and send it to us by 31st December 1997. The first five correct entries picked after the closing date will each win a year's subscription to the Mills & Boon series of their choice. What could be easier?

SPADE
SUNSHINE
PICNIC
BEACHBALL
SWIMMING
SUNBATHING
CLOUDLESS
FUN
TOWEL
SAND
HOLIDAY

W	Q	T	U	H	S	P	A	D	E	M	B
E	Q	R	U	O	T	T	K	I	U	I	E
N	B	G	H	L	H	G	O	D	W	K	A
I	I	O	A	I	N	E	S	W	Q	L	C
H	N	U	N	D	D	F	W	P	E	O	H
S	U	N	B	A	T	H	I	N	G	L	B
N	S	E	A	Y	F	C	M	D	A	R	A
U	B	P	K	A	N	D	M	N	U	T	L
S	E	N	L	I	Y	B	I	A	N	U	L
H	B	U	C	K	E	T	N	S	N	U	E
T	A	E	W	T	O	H	G	H	O	T	F
C	L	O	U	D	L	E	S	S	P	W	N

Please turn over for details of how to enter ☞

C7F

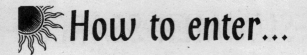# How to enter...

Hidden in the grid are eleven different summer related words. You'll find the list beside the word puzzle overleaf and they can be read backwards, forwards, up, down and diagonally. As you find each word, circle it or put a line through it. When you have found all eleven, don't forget to fill in your name and address in the space provided below and pop this page in an envelope (you don't even need a stamp) and post it today. Hurry competition ends 31st December 1997.

Mills & Boon Summer Search Competition
FREEPOST, Croydon, Surrey, CR9 3WZ
EIRE readers send competition to PO Box 4546, Dublin 24.

Please tick the series you would like to receive if you are a winner
Presents™ ❑   Enchanted™ ❑   Temptation® ❑
Medical Romance™ ❑   Historical Romance™ ❑

Are you a Reader Service™ Subscriber?   Yes ❑   No ❑

Ms/Mrs/Miss/Mr _____
                                              (BLOCK CAPS PLEASE)

Address _____

_____

_____ Postcode _____

(I am over 18 years of age)

One application per household. Competition open to residents of the UK and Ireland only.
You may be mailed with other offers from other reputable companies as a result of this application. If you would prefer not to receive such offers, please tick box. ❑   C7F

Mills & Boon® is a registered trademark of
Harlequin Mills & Boon Limited.

mps MAILING PREFERENCE SERVICE